A CATALOGUE OF THE
CLOWES COLLECTION

by

A. IAN FRASER

with a Preface by Carl J. Weinhardt

ON THE COVER:

TRIUMPHANT ENTRY OF CONSTANTINE INTO ROME, 1620-1622
Peter Paul Rubens, Flemish (1577-1640)
oil on panel, 19" x 25 1/2"

(see page 124)

CREDITS

Director, C. J. Weinhardt
Editor and Designer of Museum Publications, R. L. Warrum
Type: 8, 9 and 11 pt. Baskerville

Printing, Speedway Press, Inc., Indianapolis
Binding, H. & H. Bookbinding, Indianapolis
Color Separations, Ropkey Colorgraphics

Library of Congress Catalog Card Number 72-93036

TABLE OF CONTENTS

Page

Portraits of Dr. & Mrs. G. H. A. Clowes..................................viii-ix
Preface.. xi
Introduction...xiv
Notes to the Catalogue... xvi
Acknowledgements...xvii
About the Pictures..xix
 The Italian Pictures...xx
 The Spanish Pictures..xxvii
 The Dutch Pictures..xxxiii
 The English Pictures.. xxxvi
 The Flemish Pictures...xl
 The French Pictures...xliv
 The German Pictures.. xlvi
Italian School...1
Spanish School... 47
Dutch School.. 77
English School.. 89
Flemish School..101
French School.. 139
German School...171
Objects in the Clowes Collection... 185
Alphabetical Index of Artists...189
Board of Trustees of the Indianapolis Museum of Art........................ 193
Staff of the Indianapolis Museum of Art.....................................195

DR. GEORGE HENRY ALEXANDER CLOWES (1877-1958)
Pietro Pezzati, American (born 1902)
oil on canvas, 48" x 36"
The Clowes Collection

MRS. EDITH WHITEHILL CLOWES (1886-1967)
Pietro Pezzati, American (born 1902)
oil on canvas, 48" x 36"
The Clowes Collection

PREFACE

Writing a few words of preface to this catalogue is perhaps the happiest act of my museum career. I have had the great pleasure of knowing the collection since childhood, and my early visits to Westerley, of which I have vivid memories today, were certainly a major factor in my own decision much later to pursue the study of art history.

The joining of the Clowes Fund Collection with those of the Museum was without question the most important single event in the ninety-year history of this institution, which now bears the name of the Indianapolis Museum of Art. It has in one stroke doubled the importance of the Museum's holdings in the field of old master European paintings. The solution of housing it in a separate but connected pavilion was the perfect one, for it has allowed the collection to retain its strong personal character and individuality. Thus it can still be enjoyed in the wonderful intimacy of a domestic setting which has always been one of its greatest joys.

The Pavilion is in itself a work of art, and much credit for this must go to Mr. Allen W. Clowes, Dr. and Mrs. George H. A. Clowes, Jr., and their son Alec, all of whom played active roles during the years of painstaking planning which preceded its dedication and opening in April of 1972. Working with these members of the family was an unmitigated pleasure for both the architects and the Museum Staff. Indeed, the whole project might very accurately be described as a happy labor of love, and the result I believe reflects this in every respect. The fortuitous and admittedly unanticipated fact, that the court-yard has proved to be a superb setting for the presentation of classical music, would surely have given Mrs. Clowes great pleasure.

One aspect of this admirable accomplishment has thus far gone without official mention. It has been the tacit understanding of all involved that this Pavilion would in effect be a memorial to Edith Whitehill Clowes. Clowes Hall was created in memory of her husband, the late Dr. G. H. A. Clowes. Mrs. Clowes was founder and patron of many causes and institutions which we now accept as integral parts of the richer traditions of the life we now enjoy in Indianapolis. No one knows the full extent of the list, but one must cite at least a few of the better known: Orchard School which she helped found in 1922; the Park School Garden Tour for which she was the first chairman in 1935 and which continues to be a significant scholarship-benefit in this community. She was a pioneer in the local Planned Parenthood Center and served both as its President and a Director, as well as being a member of the first board of the Child Guidance Clinic of Marion County and founded and operated the Indianapolis Officers Club during World War II.

Mrs. Clowes was born in Buffalo, New York, the daughter of Dr. and Mrs. Frank Whitehill Hinkel. Her parents had been among the founders of the Franklin School there, which she attended before going to Vassar College, where she was a member of the class of 1907. She completed her formal education with two years of further studies in Europe.

There is little need in this context to dwell much on her uniquely alive interest in all the arts, including of course architecture and horticulture — as witness her contributions to the creation of one of our most distinguished landmarks in terms of both the building and the gardens — Trinity Church. In fact her manner, her poise, her way of life, her concern for the gifted and lasting values, her disdain for the fraudulent, and transitory, and far from least her honesty and directness, were in composite an extraordinary work of art in her own lifetime.

To a rare degree she understood her milieu, the world she lived in — its virtues and vices — but most importantly, its potentialities. Edith Whitehill Clowes was a humanitarian, with a profound sense of dignity and belief in the lasting achievements of mankind. This Pavilion is a fitting memorial to a spirit that is increasingly rare today.

The generosity of the Clowes Fund gift to the Building Fund was such that we were able to include a number of additional galleries in the Pavilion in which we have installed the Museum's own collection of Medieval and Renaissance art. It further permitted the creation of the J. M. W. Turner suite which now houses the unique and superb Katherine and Kurt F. Pantzer collection of that master's work. This collection will be subject of a later, similar catalogue. Indianapolis has obviously been blessed with a number of public-spirited citizens who have followed the splendid American tradition of collecting initially for private, but eventual public pleasure.

We are extremely fortunate to have had the services of Mr. A. Ian Fraser, Research Curator of the Clowes Fund Collection to prepare and write this catalogue. He has known the collection intimately and studied it in depth for more than a decade. He has been fortunate in having access to the exhaustive records of the collection which have been painstakingly assembled for over thirty years by the family, and most particularly, Mr. Allen W. Clowes.

I commend the result to you for study — and pleasure.

Carl J. Weinhardt

INTRODUCTION

The old saying that the pen is mightier than the sword, suggests the liberal interpretation that a cultured mind influences mankind more than other means. Dr. and Mrs. George Henry Alexander Clowes, having developed such minds, devoted the greater part of their lives toward enriching the cultural life of Indianapolis. The great enthusiasm with which they pursued their goal was felt by all who knew them. The result was the strengthening of the initial foundations upon which stand most of the artistic institutions by which our city is now enriched. High on their list of priorities stood the John Herron Art Museum, forerunner of the Indianapolis Museum of Art. Dr. Clowes served as a director of the John Herron Art Institute from 1933 until his death in 1958 and as chairman of various committees. Both Dr. and Mrs. Clowes served on the Fine Arts Committee for a number of years, playing a vital role in the acquisition of many of the most important treasures in the Museum's Collections.

Dr. Clowes was born in East Anglia in 1877; that part of England which built its great Gothic Churches with wealth amassed in the wool trade with Europe. Ipswich, his birthplace, had seen a number of his ancestors involved in the Anglican Church, and Cardinal Wolsey founded the Grammar School which he attended. His uncle, George Clowes, encouraged his scientific bent, so he went first to the Royal College of Science in London, and then to the University of Goettingen where he earned the degree of Doctor of Philosophy in Chemistry, at the age of twenty-one. During post-graduate work at the Sorbonne in Paris, he accepted an offer to become co-Director at the Gratwick Cancer Research Laboratories (now Roswell Park Memorial Institute) at Buffalo, New York, where he settled in 1901.

On June 9, 1910, Alec, as he was known to his friends, married Edith Whitehill Hinkel whose father was a leading doctor in Buffalo. Punctuated by extended visits to England, and active duty with the Chemical Warfare Service during World War I, they lived in Buffalo and started a family. They had three sons, the eldest died in infancy. The two younger boys, now Dr. George Clowes of Dover, Massachusetts, and Mr. Allen Clowes of Indianapolis, have become very active and discerning patrons of the arts in their own right.

The family moved to Indianapolis in 1919, when Dr. Clowes accepted the post of Research Associate with Eli Lilly and

Company. Two years later he became Director of Research, a position which he held until his retirement in 1946. During these years he did much to help build the Company into the pharmaceutical giant which it has become. Among his many notable contributions was the instrumental part which he played in the development of insulin during the early 1920's.

Having been in love with the art of the Old Masters all his life, Dr. Clowes found himself in the fortunate position of being able to buy fine paintings during the Depression, a time when many of the great European collections were coming onto the market. Gradually, a collection developed in the Clowes' family home, Westerley, in Golden Hill, an area of Indianapolis. He bought from established dealers, choosing, for the most part, small but exquisite works by famous artists, reinforcing his own judgement with written opinions by the leading scholars of the day. During the ensuing years, art historians have studied a number of the paintings in the Clowes Collection, sometimes filling gaps in the provenance, and sometimes suggesting a shift in attribution. As a scientist, Dr. Clowes was always searching after truth, and would have been fascinated by the findings concerning some of the paintings which have been made in the years since his death.

Following the death of Dr. Clowes in 1958, the Collection of paintings and objects d'art, which he and Mrs. Clowes had formed, became the property of the Clowes Fund, which was established as a charitable organization. A Memorial Exhibition was held at the John Herron Art Museum from October 3 to November 1, 1959, giving the Indianapolis public its first look at the most important collection of old master paintings ever assembled by one man in the history of Indiana. David G. Carter did an excellent catalogue of the exhibition. The next year, Westerley was opened, by appointment, as a "house-type" Museum. The obvious enjoyment with which people viewed the paintings, hung among fine furnishings and antiques, brought so many requests for openings, that it was soon decided to open the house twice weekly for four hours each of the two days. An average of two thousand people a year visited the collection to take guided tours. Meanwhile, Mrs. Clowes continued to make Westerley her home, and, with the help of Mr. Allen Clowes, to add a number of important canvases to the Collection.

Before the death of Mrs. Clowes in 1967, the ultimate home for the pictures was in serious doubt. On the one hand, Westerley was unique in the Mid-West. It gave people from all walks of life enormous pleasure to share in the ambiance of a connoisseur. On the other, the house had not been built as a museum, and consequently, was subject to the twin hazards of fire and theft. Indeed, no insurance was possible without twenty-four-hour guard service, an omnipresence which makes a house somewhat less than a home. At the same time, the new Indianapolis Museum of Art was taking shape at "Oldfields", the magnificent estate of Mr. Josiah K. Lilly, Jr., which had been given by his children, Josiah K. Lilly III, and Mrs. Guernsey Van Riper for that purpose. Mrs. Clowes was most enthusiastic about the new Museum, and she left the disposition of the Clowes Fund Paintings to the discretion of her sons.

She loved beauty and flowers, so her sons settled on a solution which would have delighted their Mother. They chose to dedicate a pavilion to her memory, built around a plant-filled courtyard housing the Clowes Collection in a series of intimate rooms evoking the character of Westerley. The building, known as the Clowes Pavilion, is connected to the principal museum building by a glass, enclosed, passage. Westerley closed to the public in the Summer of 1971. The Clowes Pavilion, containing all the treasures listed in this catalogue, opened in April 1972.

A.I.F.

NOTES TO THE CATALOGUE

The purpose of this *Bulletin/Catalogue* is to provide a complete list of the Clowes Fund Collection, which is on "long-term" loan to the Indianapolis Museum of Art, and which is exhibited in the Clowes Pavilion of the Indianapolis Museum of Art.

The text, while it includes relevant scholarly references, is written for the enjoyment of all lovers of art. Each painting, or pair of paintings, is illustrated to the right of the appropriate text.

The paintings have been grouped according to country of origin. Within each country they are listed chronologically with respect to the estimated date of the artist's birth. A list of art-objects follows the paintings, and will be the subject of a future Bulletin article.

All dimensions in this catalogue are given in inches with height preceding width.

A.I.F.

ACKNOWLEDGEMENTS

It is virtuously impossible to thank all those who have contributed in one way or another to making a publication such as this a reality. Nevertheless, there are some who have put in work far beyond the call of duty, to give this catalogue what virtues it may possess, and others without whom the project could not even have been undertaken.

Foremost in the list is the Clowes family. I am deeply indebted to them and hope that they will find their faith in me justified, and the resultant catalogue worthy of a noble collection. In particular, I must thank Allen Clowes, who, over many years, has built up and maintained the Clowes archives, which have been my primary sources. Without his painstaking work, and helpful encouragement at all times, the task of organizing the material would have been extremely difficult.

Various members of the Museum staff have given unstintingly of their time. I am grateful to Martha Blocker, Mary Marley and Ellen Lee for ferreting out sundry information in the I.M.A. Library, and to Paul Spheeris and Martin Radecki of the I.M.A. Laboratory for technical examinations, which they carried out on a number of the paintings. Carla Peters deserves special thanks for miraculously transforming my scrawl into print. Her wide knowledge of foreign languages was most helpful. Thanks go also to Ambrose Smith for undertaking the necessary task of proof-reading. And, finally, bouquets to Carl Weinhardt, Richard Warrum and Jeffrey Brown for a wide variety of useful suggestions and contributions. I am also greatly indebted to Mark Roskill who had had some of the paintings examined at the Fogg Museum, and whose scholarly research and opinions have been highly useful. Dr. Roskill is presently on the faculty of by the Old Masters were often superior to that of the paints produced today. Any conservator will tell you that one of his most difficult tasks is the repairing of 20th century works of art.

Let us begin with some observations about the Italian paintings in the Clowes Collection.

Chapter 1
THE ITALIAN PICTURES

The earliest painting in the Clowes Collection is the *Madonna and Child* attributed to the Badia a Isola Master (page 3). It was painted in the Tuscan hill city of Siena about 1310 A.D., some hundred years before the Renaissance started in the nearby city of Florence. While Giotto was creating monumental fresco cycles in Padua and Florence, Duccio was instilling a new tenderness, and elegance of line, into the traditional Byzantine art of Siena. Between 1308 and 1311, he created his masterpiece, an enormous altarpiece for the high altar of the Cathedral. In the center of that work, under the enthroned Virgin Mary and Christ Child, Duccio wrote, "Holy Mother of God, grant peace to Siena, grant life to Duccio, who painted thee thus." The Clowes painting is closely linked to the Madonna in Duccio's *Maesta*. Our *Madonna and Child* was probably done by the Badia a Isola Master, now thought to have been the greatest of all Duccio's pupils. Notice the tenderness implicit in the touching cheeks, and the child's arm around his mother's neck. Such a display of human emotion was virtually unknown in paintings of this period.

The greenish underpainting, which now shows through in the lower part and in the faces, is typical of the Sienese School. The brilliant red pigment used for the baby's dress was obtained by grinding the mercury oxide by hand. One only finds this pigment in the early "primitives," as it was soon discovered to be a deadly poison. The goldleaf background, representing Heaven, and the goldleaf striations in the Madonna's robe, are typically Byzantine.

The painting was probably originally an oval which would account for the unfinished lower corners. There is some damage in the lower center and if, as is likely, the work was a small devotional altarpiece, there could have been candles burning dangerously close to the paint. In any case, the majority of the original, which is still intact, is a rare treasure.

The painting attributed to Simone di Filippo da Bologna (page 5) is another Byzantine work. Because the perspective lines diverge, rather than converge, the far corner of the room appears to come forward, defying rationality, but giving the architecture a strange liveliness which contrasts charmingly with the inhabitants.

The latter consist of a weeping father on the right, with his three weeping daughters. The artist of this predella panel here illustrates one of the legends of St. Nicholas, an early Bishop of the Church, who subsequently evolved into our Santa Claus. The flood of tears has been precipitated by poverty. The house is clearly empty; the fact that it has only three walls is an artistic device to enable the viewer to see what is happening outside as well as in. The father is distressed by the fact that there are no dowries for his three marriageable daughters. Under the circumstances, he sees no prospect of finding them husbands, and neither do they.

But all is not lost. Outside stands good St. Nicholas. He pushes three bags of gold through the window, then runs away so that they will never know who befriended them. These bags were the origin of the Christmas stocking.

*   *   *

Agnolo Gaddi was a Florentine who painted in the elegant "International Gothic" manner. The *Four Saints* (page 7) offer an easy lesson in iconography. How do we know that the woman on the left is St. Mary Magdalene? After all, nobody knows what she really looked like; but if you have read your New Testament, and the lives of the Saints, you quickly get to know what attributes to look for. First, the halo 'round her head denotes sainthood. Her long blond hair, and more especially her scarlet dress, denotes Mary Magdalene, the prostitute. The desert, where she went to pray for forgiveness is symbolised by the rock with a stunted tree. In her left hand, she holds the precious cruse of ointment, with which she annointed Christ's feet. All these things clearly point to the subject as being Mary Magdalene. However, in her right hand she holds a palm branch, which is the attribute of martyrs. Here Gaddi proves his iconographic fallibility. Mary Magdalene was not martyred. The palm is simply a mistake.

St. Benedict, the founder of the order which bears his name, comes next, dressed, as is his neighbor, in the Benedictine habit. In his left hand, he holds a copy of the "Rule," which he had written, while his right hand grasps a bundle of birch twigs with which he customarily mortified his flesh.

Next comes St. Bernard of Clairveaux, recognizable by his tonsure and habit as the saint who reformed the Benedictines.

The right hand panel is occupied by St. Catherine of Alexandria, who was to be broken on a wheel for heresy. No sooner had her persecutors strapped her to it, than it miraculously fell to bits. The blessed event did her little god as the wicked men promptly decapitated her instead. Consequently, she carried the martyr's palm, to which she is entitled, and she is now standing on the broken wheel. To this day we call spinning fireworks "Catherine wheels."

*   *   *

Fra Angelico, a saintly monk who lived in Florence during the early Renaissance, painted the Nativity scene (page 9). Before 1425 A.D., no artist had painted a picture in "scientifically correct" perspective. Our little panel is no exception, although clearly the artist is struggling with the problem. In his later works he completely mastered the newly discovered "rules" of perspective.

In this early painting, not even the composition is original. He based it on a panel which is in the lower left hand corner of a great altarpiece, completed in 1423, by an artist called Gentile, who had recently moved to Florence from Fabriano. The two works are not quite alike, however. Gentile had included some people praying in the little building on the left, while he omitted the roof over the Madonna and Child. The most interesting difference between the two is on the right hand side. Gentile's panel being somewhat larger, the artist put several shepherds in a cave in the mountain between the angel and St. Joseph's head. If you look carefully at the reproduction, you will see that Fra Angelico did the same and then painted them out, presumably because it crowded and confused the composition.

Clues like this confirm the opinion that Fra Angelico did our painting after seeing the work of Gentile da Fabriano, rather than the other way around.

*   *   *

Giovanni Bellini was the most important member of a family of Venetian artists using that surname. Not only did his workshop produce a vast body of work for churches and private collectors, but he was the teacher of most of the major 16th century Venetian painters. In this period most successful "Old Masters" had a workshop full of assistants and apprentices. Scholars have devoted their lives to the problem of "how much of any particular picture is the work of the Master, and, how much was done by assistants?" In most cases, the final answer may never be found, though we may draw reasonable conclusions, based on the current evidence.

Take, for example, the Clowes' Bellini (page 13). The composition of the *Madonna and Child* is typical. He used it many times, and so did his followers, (compare it with the Niccolo Rondinelli painting in the Museum's permanent collection). But what about the child on the left? Surely he is an afterthought? If Bellini had planned a three-figure composition, wouldn't he have placed the St. John, if that is who the child is, on the right where there is ample space, rather than crowding him into a corner? If, however, the Madonna and Christ Child were already painted, the second child could only be added where he is, in order to be shown receiving Christ's blessing.

The sets of putti clustered in the background of the painting are of unusual iconographical interest. The three pink putti, which are attached to the Virgin's head, represent the Holy Spirit, and are her halo. The other four pairs represent the Aristotelian elements, of which the entire universe was then believed to be composed. The two black ones were originally blue and symbolized water, the green air, the brown earth, and the red fire. Technical examination of this picture indicates that the entire background is of a later date.

*   *   *

The author of the next painting (page 17), brings us to a problem of connoisseurship. The style is close to that of Botticelli, yet neither the drawing, nor the coloring, are quite right for him. At the same time, the disposition of the central figures is based on another picture by the master. Who then could have painted such a lovely composition? Certain elements in the figure of St. John, and especially in the landscape, seem related to the style of Piero di Cosimo. However, it is very easy to point out discrepancies between this tondo and accepted works by Piero.

We are apt to overlook the fact that an artist develops and changes a great deal during his formative years. We know that, as a very young man, Michelangelo produced the *Battle of the Centaurs*. If we did not know, wouldn't it be hard to believe that it was done by the same artist who created the *Pieta* in St. Peter's? In the same vein, it seems altogether possible that the Clowes' tondo was done by the young Piero di Cosimo during his years of apprenticeship, before he left Florence for Rome. We will probably never know, unless some now unknown documentary evidence comes to light.

*   *   *

Perugino's main claim to fame is that he was the teacher of Raphael, one of the three giants of the High Renaissance. Perugino's painting of *Christ on the Mount of Olives* (page 19), could be a study for his much larger altarpiece of the same subject in the Uffizi in Florence. The subject matter is the three disciples, Peter, James and John, asleep while Christ prays to be spared the cup of death. This accounts for the very solicitous sweet angel, frantically running through the sky bearing a golden cup. So awkward is the figure that one is tempted to suspect it of being a later addition. However, the angel in the Florentine altarpiece is even more startling, occupying as it does most of the available sky. It is dressed in a saffron apron similar to the one in the Clowes Collection, but with huge bows streaming out of the back which add to the illusion of an interplanetary maid bursting forth from the pantry of a heavenly mansion. The beautiful Umbrian landscape, receding convincingly in both linear and atmospheric perspective, is typical of the classic High Renaissance "back drop."

*   *   *

The painting by Neroccio dei Landi (page 21) is in my opinion, the finest painting in America by this 15th century Sienese master. Not only is the Madonna as lovely as any he ever painted, but it illustrates perfectly Neroccio's gift of portraying reverent tenderness devoid of mawkishness. Behind the Madonna and Christ Child are John the Baptist, on the right, and Mary Magdalene, recognizeable from the iconography previously discussed in the painting by Agnolo Gaddi. We call this painting "apocryphal," because John the Baptist was actually a baby at the same time as Christ, not a middle-aged man as shown here. Nevertheless, in Christian art it is a very common practice to have distorted time sequences in order to foretell future events. The spandrels contain the coats of arms of the Chigis and Saracenis, two of Siena's most illustrious families, and the painting was almost certainly part of a marriage dowry involving those two families. When this work was recently cleaned in the Museum's conservation laboratory, the paint surface was found to be covered with the original protective wax which had been put on by the artist. A five hundred year old picture as untouched as that is almost unknown.

Titian, a pupil of Giovanni Bellini, was the leading Venetian artist of the Renaissance. As a close friend of Doges and nobles, he was immensely successful, not only with his superb portraits, but equally in his religious and mythological paintings. How old he was at his death in 1576, nobody knows. Traditionally, he was 99, though modern scholarship takes issue with this claim. In any case, he outlived all of the other masters of his generation. Even his demise is seldom attributed to old age. Some say he fell off a ladder while painting, others that he caught the plague.

At any rate, he painted a vast number of pictures. Many of them are in dispute with regard to absolute authorship (page 27). Whether it is by the hand of the Master, or a member of his studio, in any case, it is a portrait of the Grand Chancellor of Venice, Andrea dei Franceschi, a lifelong friend of the artist and the subject of a number of Titian's portraits. One is in the National Gallery in Washington, D.C., and another is in the Detroit Institute of Arts. The Clowes' painting is much later than the other two, in both of which Franceschi is shown with brown hair, and slightly thinning bangs. One thing is certain: the subject aged with grace and grandeur.

*   *   *

Luini painted in Milan, where he was influenced by Leonardo da Vinci. Scarcely a dozen paintings can be attributed, with any degree of certainty, to Leonardo. An early portrait in the National Gallery is the only example in the United States. Therefore, we are fortunate in having a superb Luini (page 29) to help us understand Leonardo's contribution to later 16th century painting. Da Vinci eschewed the crystal clarity of the earlier Renaissance and introduced a technique known as "sfumato." It is as if one were seeing the scene in a gentle early morning haze, and Luini uses the technique most effectively in the Clowes' painting. Notice how it enables him to bestow a reasonable facsimile of the famous *Mona Lisa* smile on the Madonna, by losing the corners of the mouth and eyes in mist. Incidentally, the back of this picture bears the Sforza coat of arms, so doubtless it originally belonged to the Duke of Milan.

*   *   *

The wings of the little triptych (page 31) have been attributed to Domenico Beccafumi. He was the last important artist of the Sienese School. Perhaps his greatest work had been to design parts of the unique floor of Siena Cathedral. Like many artists of his time Beccafumi painted in Rome for a period, but after his return to Siena in 1513, his work began to show characteristics of the next generation of painters, which makes him one of the earliest Mannerists. The carving in this altarpiece is somewhat older than the painted wings. The latter were probably added as part of a wedding dowry, since if you look at the back of them, you will see the two families' coats of arms. In all likelihood, the saints are the patron saints of the families involved. On the left is John the Baptist, whose symbol, the Lamb of God, is in his left hand. On the right is St. Francis of Assisi. He is easily recognized by the nail wounds in his hands and feet. Like St. Catherine of Siena, he is said to have had a vision of Christ crucified, whereupon he received the so-called "stigmata."

*   *   *

Narrative pictures which tell a continuing story were a frequent Medieval and Renaissance device. Such a one is the predella panel by Foschi (page 33). The three monks on the right are all the same man, St. Philip Benizzi. The story begins at the left, in the scene reproduced in the enlarged detail. St. Benizzi has just happened upon three gamblers, whom he castigates for their sins. The onslaught of ribald profanity, which his rebuke precipitated, so angers him that he turns away in order to decide what to do about these wicked men. In scene two he is the right hand figure rushing back, almost tripping over himself, while he calls on the Almighty for aid. The denouement shows St. Benizzi in the middle of the composition, directing the sinners' attention to the scene behind them, as God smites the tree with a thunderbolt. Heavenly vengeance is obviously both swift and effective.

*   *   *

The painting of *Apollo and the Muses* (page 35) is a good example of the type of active, asymetrical composition which replaced the formal balance basic to earlier Renaissance composition. In the newly enlightened state of 16th century Venetian society, the nudity of the gods and goddesses was not shocking. In this particular example, Apollo is descending among the nine Muses, each of whom represents one of the Arts. Tintoretto, the leading Venetian Mannerist, painted a larger version of this picture, which belongs to Queen Elizabeth II of England. For years it hung at Hampton Court Palace; however, it has recently been moved to Windsor Castle.

Caravaggio has often been called the "Father of Baroque painting."
After a long eclipse, he is now recognized as one of the most
important forces in the entire history of Western art. As a
reaction against the overly elegant distortions of Mannerism he
introduced realism into his figures to a new, and then upsetting
degree. He also introduced dramatic "trap-door" lighting, which
directed a concentrated light on the main center of interest, while
contrasting strongly with the surrounding shadows. This lighting
technique or "tenebroso" was subsequently adopted and developed
into a more refined and subtle style in the work of Rembrandt
(see Chapter 3), who, incidentally, was only four years old at the
time of Caravaggio's untimely death.

Sleeping Cupid (page 43) is one of the greatest treasures in the
Clowes Collection. Indeed, it is one of the less than half a dozen
Caravaggios in America. It is the better of two versions of this
work. The other, long believed to be the first version, is in the
Pitti Palace in Florence. X-rays of the Indianapolis canvas have
shown much of the original sketching or "pentimenti" under-
neath the paint, with which the artist experimented while he was
trying to settle on the final composition. Again, this is very often
the most conclusive evidence as to which of two versions of a
picture is the original. The Clowes' work, for instance, has the
sketch of another head under the background in the top left
hand corner, which the artist elected to eliminate in his final version.

For a long time this picture was in a convent in Ireland. It had
been heavily overpainted to convert the exhausted or even dead (?)
Cupid into a Christ Child, crowned with thorns and surrounded
by an aura of light. The damage to the wing in the upper part
of the picture may have occurred before or after the overpainting.
In any case, these later additions were fastidiously removed in
the Museum's laboratory, exposing once again what remains of
the original wing.

*   *   *

The two tiny paintings by Francesco Guardi (page 45) bring us to
the end of the Italian pictures. Guardi was an 18th century artist
whose main market was for scenes of Venice which were sold
to aristocratic tourists making the obligatory "Grand Tour."
The wealthiest travelers would return home laden with large
canvases depicting all the city's major views. People of more
modest means, however, bought smaller postcard-size souvenirs
which were frequently called capriccios such as these. They were

inventions or fantasies which included several famous monuments and buildings often miles apart. Three splendid large capriccios by Pannini are in the permanent collection of the Indianapolis Museum of Art. Sometimes, as in the case of the two Guardis', the pictures were what one might describe as "typical views" without being "specific." While many 18th century artists catered to the tourist trade, Canaletto and Guardi stand apart as the most imaginative and brilliant of the Venetian landscape painters, regardless of their motivation.

Chapter 2
THE SPANISH PICTURES

The earliest Spanish paintings in the Clowes Collection date from about 1400 A.D. (page 49). These two panels are probably from a large altarpiece or "retable," as there are at least six other panels from the same set in the United States. While nothing is known of Pere Vall, the artist to whom these works are attributed, he is now thought to be the same person as the "Master of the Cardona Pentecost."

Many an artist whose name is lost in oblivion has subsequently been christened by scholars as "the master of 'this' " or of 'that'. This happens when a number of works are found to be attributable to the same hand. As in this case, the master is named after the major work in his theoretically assembled oeuvre. On other occasions he may be named after the owner of one of his paintings. In such a case, a scholar has usually been working on attributions for a collector, with a particular unsigned work being the key to his research (such as the example here) and sometimes the master is named for a date (such as the Master of 1505) or for the type of painting in which he specialized. Occasionally, their names can be quite entertaining, such as the "Master of a Thousand Virgins," another 15th century Spanish painter who painted an altarpiece of St. Ursula with her thousand maidens.

If we examine the Pere Vall panels, we can enjoy another lesson in iconography. Doubtless, you've already identified St. Mary Magdalene carrying the ubiquitous cruse of ointment. She stands next to St. Stephen, shown holding his Testament and martyr's palm. He was stoned to death, hence the stone on top of his bleeding head. In the second panel, the ponderous looking saint in a brown cape can easily be identified by his label which he displays on his chest. It reads "S. Amador." Latin scholars

will instantly know that he has something to do with "love."
His story explains how he got both his name and his expression.
As a simple-minded peasant he took his betrothed to a senile
priest to say their marriage vows. Since the young couple spoke
no Latin, they relied on the priest to prompt them whenever
a response was called for. This the old man did, until at the end
of the ceremony, he was chagrined to discover that, by mistake,
he had performed the wrong service. Instead of being married,
the young man had taken the vows of a monk. It was too late to
undo what had been done. Marriage was an impossibility after
swearing eternal chastity before the Lord. History does not relate
what happened to his fiancee, but the young man entered
a monastery, where he adopted for his name the Latin word which
he had learned the hard way. St. Michael, the remaining Saint,
is easy to recognize. Like St. George, he slew a dragon, but St.
Michael was an Archangel, and, as everybody knows, even rank
and file angels have wings for transportation. St. George always
gets around on a horse.

*   *   *

Not too many people have heard of Dominico Theotocopuli, but
millions know the artist's Spanish nickname. Finding his real
name a tongue-twister, the Spanish called him El Greco, which
simply means "The Greek." Born in Crete, he moved to Italy
as a young man and developed a highly personal Mannerist style
under the influence of Venetian painters in general, and Tintoretto
in particular. He finally settled in Toledo, Spain, where he spent
the second half of his life. The *Head of Christ Bearing the Cross*
(page 57) was a favorite subject with El Greco. Note especially the
dramatic forced perspective and the tear-filled eyes. Technical
examinations of the edges of this canvas reveal that it has been
cut down from a larger work, though there is no way of knowing
when or why this was done. Presumably, Christ is carrying the
cross to Calvary rather than being crucified, as he appears to be
fully clothed.

*   *   *

El Greco's son was also an artist. We really don't know whether he
had anything to do with the painting which we call *St. Thomas*
(page 59) or how much of it might be by him or be the work of
assistants. While the work is clearly "School of El Greco," we
can be reasonably sure that little, if any, of the painting was done
by the Master. The figure of the saint is too harsh and ill-pro-

xxix

portioned, and the two halves of the landscape, which happens to be a view of Toledo, show the distinctive brushstrokes of more than one artist. Harold Wethey, a distinguished scholar at the University of Michigan, attributed this painting to Luis Tristan, a slightly later Spanish artist. While it bears certain characteristics of his style, Tristan was noted for his sensitive delineation of the human hand. A quick glance at the gesturing right hand in the Clowes picture will suffice to show that whoever painted it could barely count fingers, as the middle finger appears to be an after-thought. It is the right hand that leads some people to believe that the subject is St. Thomas. It looks as though he is asking Christ to show him the nail wounds in his hands and feet.

*　　*　　*

St. Matthew (page 51), *St. Simon* (page 55), and *St. Luke, Bartholomew* or *Mark* (page 55) are three of a series of nine paintings of Christ and His disciples. The obvious freedom with which they are painted has prompted scholars to date them from the last period of El Greco's life. For centuries they hung unframed between the clerestory windows of the Church of the Almadrones, near Guadalajara, about twenty-five miles northeast of Madrid. During the Spanish civil war, the roof was blown off the church, and the officer in charge sent the paintings to the Prado Museum in Madrid for safekeeping. After the war the government needed money, so they sold five of the pictures to the United States, and then decreed that no other El Greco's were ever to leave Spain. Dr. Clowes had his choice of canvasses. He selected these three. The fourth is now in the Kimbell Collection in Fort Worth, Texas, and the fifth is in the Los Angeles County Museum. The other paintings of the series of Christ and three disciples are still in the Prado.

El Greco did not use traditional iconography, so one cannot conclusively identify each saint. However, note that he rotated the colors, so that each disciple wears a color of his own and one borrowed from his neighbor. The three magnificent frames, which are not exactly alike, were skillfully altered to fit the paintings. The haunting beauty of these splendid pictures will unfold in proportion to the time you can give to them in the small so-called Clowes Chapel.

*　　*　　*

Though Ribera was a Spanish painter, he spent much of his life in Italy where he was strongly influenced by the work of Caravaggio.

xxx

He painted *Archimedes* (page 61) while he was living in Naples. Pride in his nationality is apparent from the inclusion of the word "espanol," which he added to his signature, on the piece of paper in the subject's left hand. Originally, this was one of a set of six paintings of philosophers. Until recently, they all belonged to the Prince of Lichtenstein, who still owns one of the world's greatest art collections.

The Clowes' painting shows the consummate skill with which Ribera could paint an old man's face and rheumatic hands. He wears a ragged outer cloak for the protection of his more "proper" clothing; a similar coat is shown in the *Water Carrier of Seville,* by Velazquez.

*   *   *

You are forgiven if you made the natural mistake of thinking that the School of Zurbaran painting (page 63) is of St. Stephen. A little knowledge of iconography can be misleading. Certainly the subject is of a saint being stoned, but this martyr wears a Dominican habit, garb of the order founded in the 13th century, which makes him over a 1000 years too late to be that first century Christian martyr. The fact is that we don't know who this is meant to be. This picture comes from a series of at least thirty-eight martyrs which Zurbaran's workshop did for the lower cloister of the Barefoot Mercedarians, which is attached to the Church of San Jose, Seville. Test your connoisseurship by comparing this painting with the Zurbaran of *St. Francis in Prayer,* which is in the I.M.A. permanent collection. As haunting, imaginative and fine as the Clowes' painting is, it is difficult to accept it as by the hand of the Master himself.

*   *   *

Velazquez was the court painter to Philip IV of Spain. Today, with a Zurbaran still-life fetching over three million dollars, and a portrait by the same artist going for more than five, it is small wonder that the question of who painted this *Still-Life* (page 65) is of considerable interest to many people.

The technique, and the quality of paint and canvas, immediately remind one of Velazquez. However, the composition, if it were by him, would be unique. The problem might be insoluble, but for one fact: the picture has been cut from a larger work. It certainly extended beyond the left of the existing portion, and probably both above and below it. Vestiges of plants, furniture and fabric can all be seen on the left. It seems entirely possible that a large portrait was planned originally, but that for some reason the sitter, or sitters, never returned to have the work completed. If Velazquez did not paint this still-life, then it must be the work of an exceptionally skilled imitator.

*   *   *

The identity of the lady (page 67) is not known. Whatever her true identity may be, she poses an instructive object-lesson for those who, like her, follow the dictates of fashion. She is dressed in the style of Philip IV's Court, the wide panels of crimped hair being a reflection of the extended paniers, or farthingales, which would have sprung out from her waist, in short, a style of dress that we find, even with our outlandish styles, rather bizarre.

People with square faces, who wear square hairstyles, while underlining it all with such a neckline, are inevitably going to look their worst. If you recoil in horror the first time you meet this lady, try taking another look. Forget her hair and dress and concentrate on the face alone. Now, don't you think that she looks a levelheaded and intelligent woman? She might even have a sense of humor.

*   *   *

The painting by Murillo (page 69) is a typical Spanish interpretation of the Virgin Mary. Historians tell us that Christ came from a tribe of dark swarthy Jews. Raphael invented the lovely fair Madonna to which so many of us have become conditioned. Admitting the fact that she is depicted as far too young to be praying over the crown of thorns and nails with which her thirty-three year old son has just been crucified, Murillo's vision of her is probably much closer than Raphael's to the way she might have looked.

*   *   *

The Game of Staves, or *El Juego de Barras,* as the picture is called (page 71), puts one in mind of Goya's masterpiece *The Shooting of the 3rd of May 1808.* It has some of the same intensity which one experiences in that life and death drama. Here the champion is challenging anyone to a game. It is played by two men, each armed with a club. One holds his above the head to ward off a blow from the other. They alternate roles, faster and faster, till a club is broken or a skull cracked. Such a fearsome sport is no less than one could expect from the land of bullfights.

An interesting fact about this panel is that it is painted over a 15th century Spanish Primitive of three saints in a landscape. The older painting was done the other way up, so that the right hand edge was its base. If you look carefully at the reproduction, you can see traces of plants in the dark areas on the right, and when you look at the painting itself, you will discover several more. X-rays of the old picture showed that the primitive is far too badly damaged to be reconstructed.

*   *   *

The little girl on a green cushion (page 73) is one of the most popular paintings in the Clowes Collection. It probably predates *The Game of Staves* by twenty to thirty years. Notice how beautifully the fine hair of a child has been captured. If we think our children grow up too fast, consider this young lady. She surely hasn't reached her third birthday, and yet she is dressed like a little old lady. She even has her ears pierced and is holding a fan. Worst of all, she must remain erect or suffer the consequences of the whalebones inserted in her corset. Small wonder that she looks so pitiful.

Chapter 3
THE DUTCH PICTURES

We speak of the 17th century in Holland as "The Golden Age of Dutch Painting." Frans Hals was the earliest of the major painters of the period. He was a jovial fellow with a weakness for wine, women and song, symptoms of which are all too apparent in his *Self Portrait* (page 79). At one time this picture was overpainted as a woman. When a technical examination was carried out about 1934, it revealed a self-portrait, which most experts agreed was the lost original from which several copies had been made. At that time, the painting was in the hands of a New York dealer. The discovery was so sensational that Sir Kenneth Clark, then Keeper of London's National Gallery, sailed for New York in an attempt to buy the picture for England. However, the journey from Indianapolis to New York City by train was shorter, and Dr. Clowes acquired the treasure.

A remarkably candid study, the artist here makes no attempt to minimize the ravanges which time and dissipation have wrought upon his face. It was painted late in life, when the impoverished Hals was living in the Almshouse in Haarlem (now the Frans Hals Museum). Black and white being by far the cheapest oil colors, Hals was in the habit of using all other colors rather sparingly. Indeed, he is sometimes known as the artist who painted in a hundred shades of black.

*   *   *

Once Holland had wrested its independence from Spain, its prosperity depended largely on international trade. Consequently, ships flying the Dutch flag became symbols of power and profit. Seascapes, such as the one by Abraham Willaerts (page 81), were immensely popular. A burgeoning middle class was rapidly developing a taste for paintings to hang in the home, and pleasant and optimistic subjects such as this were just what they wished.

*   *   *

"What, no Rembrandts?" I said in jest to a distinguished Dutch collector of 17th century paintings as he showed me around his home in Amsterdam. "How could I," he replied, "when Rembrandt is known to have painted about seven hundred pictures, three thousand of which are in the United States?" The problem is that a genius such as Rembrandt had many close followers and students. Consequently, it is a monumental task for scholars to decide how much of the vast body of work which is attributed to Rembrandt is indeed his. Take for example his *Self Portrait* (page 83). It is signed exactly the way it would have been had it been painted when he was about 23 and living in Leiden. We can trace it back well into the 18th century, so we know that it is no modern fake. However, there are two other versions of this picture. It does not seem likely that such a creative an artist, who did self-portraits for practice, would ever have done the same image three times. Even the signature is not proof of authenticity, as many collectors added signatures long after the artist was dead. There is general agreement among scholars that the Clowes' self-portrait is the best of the known versions, and therefore is probably by Rembrandt. There is, of course, also the possibility that it is the finest extant copy of a lost original. After all, until the Frans Hals self-portrait was discovered, several copies, including one in the Metropolitan Museum in New York, were thought to be the original by Hals.

It must be admitted that the problem of authorship is a matter of educated guesswork. The Sistine Chapel ceiling would be so awkward to move, that it is obvious that the frescoes painted upon it are the ones which were commissioned by Pope Julius II from Michelangelo. But what about the *Mona Lisa*? There are many versions of it, some claiming to be the original by Leonardo da Vinci. We know that King Francis I of France bought *Mona Lisa* from Leonardo's estate after the artist's death, and we take it for granted that the painting hanging in the Louvre in Paris is that picture. Furthermore, connoisseurs agree that the Louvre work must be the original, because it is the finest existing version of the subject. We still can't be absolutely certain that it is not a superb early copy, substituted when the original was stolen in August 1911. As a point of interest, the Louvre authorities were so shaken by the theft that they immediately hung a copy in its place, while keeping the loss a secret. For eighteen months, the public admired a fake. Nobody questioned the changling. In December 1913, the *Mona Lisa* which we see hanging in the Louvre today was mysteriously found, but if we had the power to bring Leonardo back from the dead, even he probably couldn't tell us whether it's his or not.

In the early 1950's, an unsigned Cubist painting came up for auction. Braque and Picasso were both asked about it. They agreed that one of them had painted it, but neither was sure whether it was his or his friend's. We should always bear such possibilities in mind when we hear "great experts" waxing dogmatic.

In any case, our *Self Portrait* is a superb and highly admired work and stands an excellent chance of being by the Master himself.

*   *   *

The second painting attributed to Rembrandt is the *Portrait of an Old Man in a Tall Fur-edged Cap* (page 85). The handling of the light is much more subtle than in the earlier self-portrait, and recalls the "trap-door lighting" of Caravaggio. Rembrandt never went to Italy, so he was probably never directly exposed to the work of Caravaggio. Many of his countrymen, however, especially artists from Utrecht, settled in Rome and sent back paintings to Holland which were heavily influenced by the work of the great Italian Baroque master. Rembrandt was certainly indebted to Caravaggio's successful experiments with the use of dramatic lighting, which is not to belittle Rembrandt's achievement, for even without it, his penetrating insight into the human mind has never been surpassed.

*   *   *

While Protestant Holland generally eschewed religious painting, they loved hidden symbolism and pictures pregnant with moralizing allusions. Such a work is the flower painting by Ambrosius Bosschaert (page 87). The first thing any gardener will notice is that it is an impossible bouquet, since it includes flowers from every season of the year. This is clearly contrived to illustrate the continuity of life. The whole picture symbolized the world in microcosm. The fly in the right foreground has to fly in and out of flowers to pollinate them. In turn, he provides food for the lizard who is getting ready to pounce from behind the vase. The lizard will then fertilize the ground, enabling more flowers to grow. Even the butterfly, so gracefully alighting on the tulip, is there for a reason. It symbolizes the beautiful, but transient and ephemeral nature of life in its everychanging and unalterable progression.

Chapter 4
THE ENGLISH PICTURES

With few exceptions, England was without noteworthy painters from Carolingian times until the 18th century. To be sure, there were rich art patrons, but, for the most part, they bought European masters and commissioned new works from the leading Continental artists of the day. All the outstanding court painters were imported from across the Channel.

The earliest English portrait in the Clowes Collection, therefore, is something of an enigma (page 91). While not a major painting, it is nevertheless exceptionally competent when compared with the primitive style generally prevalent at the time. You might think that it would be a simple matter for art historians to attribute this work to a particular artist. I recall, some years ago, discussing this painting with a distinguished scholar from the National Gallery in London, England. "While it might be as late as 1650," he said, "it is probably 16th century. In any case, it is not English. I would suggest checking with the museum at Chantilly, in France, as it is clearly a follower of Clouet." It so happened that a curator of French paintings from the Louvre in Paris was visiting Indianapolis shortly after this, and I took the opportunity to ask, "Do you think that this picture could be by a follower of Clouet?" "Absolutely not," he replied. "It isn't even French, it's English!"

Since then I have discussed the picture with many authorities and studied hundreds of paintings in what has been a vain attempt to find a possible attribution. Most of the people I have talked to maintain that it is English, though a number of scholars support the French authorship, arguing that no English 17th century artist painted in such a sophisticated style. Fortunately, nobody has complicated the issue further by suggesting a third country of origin.

I have a theory that it could have been done by a very talented amateur English artist who transcended his usual limitations to paint a very beautiful portrait of his loved one. Look at the full lips and intimate gaze. What's more, she's dressed up for the occasion, in a costume, possibly one inherited from her mother or grandmother. Had it been the current fashion, she would have worn the wreath with the tear-drop pearl straight on her head, instead of sporting it at a saucy angle. My theory may be quite wrong, but unless I find evidence to the contrary, I shall continue to enjoy the possible romance.

*   *   *

If Sir Joshua Reynolds was not the greatest 18th century English painter, he was certainly the most successful. An eloquent speaker, he relished nothing more than his pedagogical discourses on painting, which he delivered annually at the banquet of the Royal Academy. He was its first founder and first president. (Interstingly enough, an American, Benjamin West, who was a disciple of Reynolds, became second President of the Royal Academy.) Modesty was hardly one of Sir Joshua's virtues. As a name-dropper he had no peer, and was known to start a conversation with the preamble: —"As I was mentioning to His Majesty, only last evening . . . " He was certainly the first English artist to climb to the top of the social ladder. In fairness, it should be noted that he did more than any other man to upgrade the quality of English painting, through the formulation of artistic standards which continued to be the yardstick of excellence to which the British adhered until the middle of the 20th century.

It was Reynolds who painted the *Portrait of Mrs. Thomas Watkinson Payler* in 1771 (page 93). He was usually inundated with commissions.

Consequently, he employed a number of artists to work for him. Some specialized in "backgrounds," other in "furniture" or "drapery," etc. It is very unlikely that any portrait, except for his early works, is entirely by Reynolds' own hand. Nobody expected otherwise, any more than one would expect a fashionable photographer to do all the work himself. Reynolds would block in the canvas at the initial sitting, then turn it over to assistants till the final sitting, when he would go over the whole picture and complete it to his client's satisfaction. He painted a pendant portrait of Mr. Thomas Watkinson Payler at the same time.

According to Reynolds' accounts, Mr. Payler paid seventy guineas for the two canvases on June 24, 1771. If you look at the Clowes' painting, it is easy to see why Reynolds was so successful. He has made Mrs. Payler into a classic beauty of the period, with a high intelligent brow, widely spaced eyes, a wistful expression, and a then fashionable consumptive pallor.

*   *   *

Compare the painting of Mrs. Payler with that of Mrs. Charles James Fox (page 95). The quality of workmanship in the former is so superior that the term "School of Reynolds" is indicated when describing the latter. As I have already implied, it is impossible to say that any portrait is entirely by Reynolds himself, but one may be reasonably sure that Mrs. Fox is mainly, if not entirely, a workshop production. It is certainly somewhat later than Mrs. Payler's portrait. The picture must have been done about 1780, as Reynolds did another documented portrait of her in 1789, in which she is clearly somewhat older. At the time of the Clowes' portrait, she was a Mrs. Armstead. She married the famous English politician, Charles James Fox, in 1795 and lived on until 1842, when she died at the age of ninety. Dr. Clowes bought and sold many paintings over the years as he refined and improved the collection, but this canvas always held a special place in his affections, as it was his first major purchase. He bought the picture on January 13, 1933.

Although Dr. Clowes owned no Turners, Turner is, fortunately, brilliantly represented in other portions of the Museum's collection. This is primarily due to the efforts of his close friends and co-collectors, Mr. and Mrs. Kurt F. Pantzer and Mr. and Mrs. Nicholas H. Noyes, whose generosity has for the most part made the extraordinary "Turner Suite" on the second floor of the Clowes Pavilion a reality and what may well become a center of Turner studies in America.

John Constable loved the English countryside so much that he never saw any good reason to look farther afield for inspiration. Though he was from Suffolk, he did much of his painting around Salisbury, in Wiltshire, where his wife had family connections. He painted the cathedral there many times, usually emphasizing its lofty spire piercing an ever changing sky.

Visitors to England are well aware of the vicissitudes of weather, and no artist has surpassed Constable in his ability to capture its changing qualities. The sky in *Harnham Bridge* (page 97) is a typical example. You can't tell if it's going to pour with rain, or if the sun is about to burst forth. The bridge is no longer standing, but otherwise the scene has changed remarkably little in the hundred and fifty years since the picture was painted. The spire of Salisbury cathedral is just visible on the right.

*　　　*　　　*

Conservative in some ways, Constable was a pioneer in others. He was the first important artist to make a habit of making oil sketches on the site. Most artists, if they ventured forth at all, executed pencil drawings, often with a few watercolor notations. Then they returned to their studios to paint the finished picture. Following Constable's example, the artist standing at his easel in a field has become the standard stereotype. He enjoyed very little success during his lifetime.

At his death in 1837, however, the government decided to buy a painting from his estate for the National Gallery in London. The canvas selected is called *The Cornfield* because a field of wheat—which the British call "corn"—can be seen in the distance. In the foreground, a small boy in a red coat is lying down getting water from a stream, while a collie dog rounds up the sheep. The Clowes' oil sketch of the same subject (page 99) is of particular interest when compared with the National Gallery painting. The final version is better composed; note the widened gap between the trees and the placing of the dog. The finished painting also uses a more varied palette. We are fortunate indeed to have this "modello" for one of his major works, executed in a wonder-fully free and fresh manner.

Chapter 5.
THE FLEMISH PICTURES

Flanders, as a country, no longer exists, though the "Flemish" language is still alive in much of Blegium. A tradition of exquisite craftsmanship and attention to detail was well established in the art of Flanders by the 14th century. Even the Florentines of the early Renaissance had high admiration for the work of the Flemish Masters. While Italians were busy mastering the art of perspective, the Flemings were developing an oil-painting technique which would enable them to render the minutest detail with unprecedented exactitude.

Three great artists, the Master of Flemalle (probably Robert Campin), Rogier van der Weyden and Jan van Eyck (and possibly his brother Hubert) are all thought to have played a role in this technical revolution. Until the early 15th century, the standard medium throughout Western Europe was egg tempera—ground pigments mixed with raw eggs. The paint, which was opaque, dried quickly and was not easily reworked. Linseed oil mixed with pigments, however, remained workable for an extended period and could be applied in layers of transparent glazes, which enabled artists to create an illusion of reality which was impossible before.

Consider the *Portrait of a Man* (page 103). Note the handling of the fur collar, an effect which could not have been achieved with the older medium. The picture was originally painted on a panel, but some years ago, due to the fragility of the panel, it was transferred to canvas. In the process the surface was badly abraded necessitating considerable treatment. Consequently, a firm attribution of authorship is difficult, if not impossible, unless some undiscovered evidence is found.

*   *   *

Hieronymus (or Jerome) Bosch painted some of the world's most extraordinary, or perhaps in contemporary terms "surrealist" religious pictures. As little is known about the artist, we cannot be sure of his motives for painting the way he did. We do know, however, that his style appealed to the religious fanaticism of Spain's King Philip II, who bought a number of his greatest altarpieces. *Ecce Homo* (page 105) depicts the moment when Christ is being shown to the citizens of Jerusalem who have to decide whether they want Him crucified or freed. The mob is screaming "let Him be crucified," while the people on the balcony would appear to personify the deadly sins. All is confusion except for the three figures to the right of the pair of columns. Pontius Pilate stands at the right holding the rope with which Christ's hands are bound. Jesus, sagging at the knees, stands by the column, apparently oblivious to the commotion. Between them stands an enigmatic figure with a face part human, part animal. What does he represent? Is he the Devil ingratiating himself to Pilate, trying to tempt Jesus, or perhaps keeping his options open? We don't know. Most viewers find this highly emotional painting unforgettable.

*   *   *

The Temptation of St. Anthony (page 107) is even more baffling. A larger, almost identical version of this altarpiece is in Lisbon, Portugal. St. Anthony, in the middle of the picture, prays for strength to resist what appear to be excessively unattractive temptations. In the Lisbon work, he is encouraged by two priests at an altar with a glowing crucifix located in the dark doorway of the delapidated tower.

*   *   *

Another picture which has so far defied interpretation is *Landscape with Hermit* (page 109). The title is merely descriptive since the subject has not been determined. Many people think that it may be another "Temptation of St. Anthony." In the top right, an avenging angel is streaking down to strike the flaming mountain with a sword. A ship is sinking in the harbor while a witch-like woman extends her arms over a cadaver floating in the murky lake. Near the bottom a sinister monster is climbing out of the lake unnoticed by the praying hermit. His habitation is half tree, half house. Strangest of all is a tattered white flag sticking out of a crack in the tree's trunk. There must be a story to tie it all together, but what it is remains a mystery.

*   *   *

The next picture (page 111), is by Adriaen Isenbrandt and might serve to throw a ray of light on the one which we have just discussed. On the left is the inn at Bethlehem. Notice the three balls on the roof, a traditional medieval inn sign. The three objects on the tree on the "Circle of Wellens de Cocq" picture look remarkably similar. In both the Isenbrandt pictures (page 113) there is a detailed distant landscape which is typical of Flemish Renaissance painting but has nothing to do with either Palestine or Egypt.

Now let us consider another aspect of Flemish religious art—the little *Holy Family with an Angel* (page 117). Exquisite though the painting may be, there is still an air of unreality about it. In particular, the Christ Child looks rather like a puppet. It is curious that the Christ Child in religious paintings is so often the most awkward part of the composition. This is partly explained by the fact that these works were Church commissions, and invariably the artist was instructed to depict the Christ Child as "wise," which is virtually an impossible look for a baby. The basic alternatives left to the painter, therefore, were to paint a "little old man" or a baby with a swollen head. In the hands of any but the most inspired artist neither alternative produces an attractive result.

In Flanders, the Holy Family was supposed to be remote from everyday life. One senses an impenetrable shield between the viewer and the viewed. The Virgin Mary seems to be raising her right hand to prevent us approaching any closer. Compare this work with a similar composition which was painted at about the same time in Italy (page 39). In the Italian work religion is brought down to earth. The Madonna is someone one might expect to meet, and the children, Christ and St. John, look and behave the way children do.

*   *   *

The Brueghel family is one of the most illustrious in the annals of Flemish painting. Pieter Brueghel the Elder is the most famous and the father of a dynasty of artists which continued for several generations. Jan the Elder was Pieter the Elder's most talented son. He is sometimes known as "The Velvet Brueghel" because of his particular taste in fabrics. His specialty was cool blue landscapes, a fine example of which is the *Canal Scene* (page 119). It belongs to a set which he did to represent the Seasons. Spring is the subject of the Indianapolis panel. Originally all four paintings were in the Royal Collection at Dresden.

*   *   *

Rubens was the most important and successful Flemish Baroque painter. He spent many years in Italy where he learned to combine the impressive scale and swirling design of Italian art with Flemish coloring and detail. His clientele included everybody who was anybody. The result was that he was obliged to employ a veritable army of assistants who helped cover acres of canvas which came from his shops. Only in his sketches can one be reasonably sure of finding his unaided hand at work. *The Triumphant Entry of Constantine into Rome* (page 125) is a superb sketch by Rubens. It is very swiftly painted in transparent oil colors. The sky is laid in with only a half dozen strokes which show through the mane of the Emperor's horse. The vitality of his brushstrokes is apparent everywhere. In the hands of a lesser Master one would expect a certain hesitancy here and there. The Clowes' sketch is one of twelve which Rubens did for Louis XIII as a set of tapestry designs telling the story of the life of the Emperor Constantine. Once the sketches had been approved, they were scaled up in Rubens' workshop to actual tapestry size on large sheets of brown paper. These are called "cartoons." At the Royal Tapestry Works, the weavers worked right up against the cartoon matching each color as they went along. All the ends of the silks would be tied off away from the paper so that the "right" side of the tapestry was against the picture. This meant that when the work was finished it would be a mirror image of the original design (i.e. reversed). Tapestry work is very painstaking. It was not unusual for a square yard to occupy one person for a year. Five of Rubens' tapestries had been completed when Cardinal Barberini traveled to Paris as Papal Nuncio. Having received them as a gift from the King, he returned to Rome where he commissioned Pietro da Cortona to redesign the rest of the series so that he could have a complete set woven in his own tapestry works. Today a set of these tapestries on the life of Constantine is in the Philadelphia Museum of Art.

*   *   *

Rubens' most gifted pupil was Sir Anthony van Dyck. Like his master, he worked in Italy for some time. He is perhaps best known, however, for the elegant portraits which he executed during the last seven years of his life while he was court painter to King Charles I of England. The *Self Portrait* (page 135) attributed to him was probably done soon after he arrived in London. There is another version of this portrait at the Palace of Versailles. A larger painting exists at the Prado in Madrid, which is a double portrait by Van Dyck of himself with Sir Endymion Porter. The self-portrait half of it is almost a replica of the Clowes painting.

*   *   *

While it was usual for successful artists to have a workshop of assistants, there are instances in which two equally talented artists painted pictures together sharing the profits. For example,

there are occasions when Rubens worked in partnership with Jan
Brueghel the Elder. In certain cases the liaison was far from
harmonious due to clashing styles. However, with Pieter Bout and
Adriaen Boudewijns (page 137) their gifts exactly complemented
each other. This is a "genre" scene packed with incident. These
small pictures were immensely popular as conversation pieces.
This example, which is roughly the size of a double page of this
book, contains over a hundred and thirty people, not to mention
animals, painted in such detail that not only can you see what
everybody is doing, but you can count the cards which the card-
players are holding. Boudewijns painted the landscape, Bout the
figures. Paintings such as this one give us a rich impression of what
life in Flanders must have been like around 1700.

Chapter 6.
THE FRENCH PICTURES

The courtly art of France is well represented in the Clowes Collection.
The most important 15th century painter was a Burgundian by the
name of Jean Fouquet. Since he devoted most of his life to
manuscript miniatures, there are only a handful of paintings which
can be attributed to him. One such is a half-length portrait of
Guillaume Jouvenal des Ursins, Chancellor to Charles VII of
France. That picture, which is the left hand panel of a lost alter-
piece, is in the Louvre in Paris, France, and has been dated about
1460. There is reason to believe that the Clowes' Fouquet (page
141) is cut out of the missing right hand section of the same altarpiece and is a portrait of Guillaume's elder brother Jean. While
the wood panels have not been examined to see if they came from
the same source, the paint surfaces have. Both works show traces
of gold-leaf under the background pigment, the heads are lighted
from a consistent light source and the color used behind the heads
is the same in both cases. To carry the conjecture further, the
lost central section of the altarpiece could have been of a Madonna
and Christ Child. The head in the Indianapolis painting has his
eyes raised in possible contemplation of the Virgin. In the Louvre
painting, the eyes are lowered to the point where one might
anticipate the placing of the Christ Child. There is more detective
work to be done on the Clowes' panel before we can be sure that
this thesis is correct. Regardless, it is a fascinating study of a head
by a great Master.

No painting in the Clowes Collection has a more clear-cut history
than the portrait of *Francois de Scepeaux* (page 143) by Francois
Clouet. It was painted in 1566 for the sitter and was in the possession
of his heirs until 1950 when Dr. Clowes bought it. Also, it is
one of the few pictures which is almost certainly in its original
frame, a superb Renaissance example set with lapis lazuli and carnelian.

*   *   *

Not much is known about Corneille de Lyon except that he was
a 16th century court painter who specialized in small portraits
generally with a plain colored background. There are three
excellent examples of his work in the Clowes Collection (pages
147, 149, and 151). The first (page 147) is the best known.
It was long thought to be a portrait of Diane de Poitiers, mistress
of King Henry II of France. It only takes a glance at a few of the
known likenesses of Diane to see that the Indianapolis lady is
somebody else. We now know that it is a portrait of Marie de
Guise who was the mother of Mary Queen of Scots.

*   *   *

One day we hope to know more about the *Abbess at Prayer*
(page 153). That she was a lady of rank is attested to by the coat
of arms in the top left which is also a clue to her identity. It is
diamond shaped because she was unmarried.

*   *   *

Claude Lorrain and Nicolas Poussin were contemporaries who
chose to live most of their lives in Rome. They are both known
for their "classical landscapes" and Claude is especially celebrated
for the soft dreamy atmosphere with which his works are inbued.
Consider the *Flight Into Egypt* (page 155). Notice that in this
period the acknowledged subject matter is given less prominence
than the setting. The latter is a typical classical landscape,
carefully balanced, so that the eye is taken back in a zig-zag
through the receding planes. Such pictures very much influenced
the English painters and landscape-architects of the 18th century.
This particular canvas was in various distinguished British collections
including that of the Earl of Iveagh whose treasures, on view at
Kenwood House, are admired by visitors to London from all over
the world.

Hubert Robert's art follows in the grand tradition begun a century earlier by Poussin and Claude Lorrain. The 18th century in France was an age of elegant interiors. Decorators often divided the walls into panels which, in turn, were designed to be filled with sets of paintings. It was a logical development from the earlier practice of hanging rooms with tapestries. Robert did many canvases for decorative purposes. *La Statue* (page 163) probably comes from such a set. Pictures of this type are called "overdoors" as they were painted to fit a specific space above a door. Story content was less important than the decorative aspects of these romantic neo-classical fantasies.

Chapter 7.
THE GERMAN PICTURES

Problem pictures are always intriguing, and the *Passion of Jesus Christ* (page 173) is indeed a problem. It is a triptych set in a modern frame. Since triptychs are usually designed to close, the side wings are half the width of the center section. In the Clowes' altarpiece the three parts are the same size. It might seem that because the twelve panels were found separately, that some are missing. Not so. The story that they tell is complete from the Last Supper to the Resurrection. Even the order of the panels cannot be changed as they relate the events sequentially.

Even more fascinating, the unknown master who painted this work around 1400, was in some respects way ahead of his time. He treated the twelve panels as a unified entity. Notice in the top row how the circular table on the left balances up with the circular throne on the right, and the rhythm of the haloes with the lancet windows. Look at the lower panels. The two crosses on the left lead one's eye into the composition and are perfectly complemented by the sarcophagi in the right hand panels. The compositional lines in all four center panels, on the other hand, are vertical.

As you can see it is quite a puzzle. It is possible that originally there was a devotional panel in the middle which was the size of four of the smaller ones. While such a solution would have solved the problem of the folding of the triptych, it is hard to see how it would have improved the overall design. Notice how graphically every symbolic detail is shown. At the Last Supper, ingeniously arranged in an upright panel, St. John literally has his head on Christ's breast. One can't help wondering how the rest of him fits under the table-cloth. Now look at the cruelty displayed in the faces of the soldiers

in the third panel where the leonine Judas is betraying Jesus with
a kiss, or in the fourth where Pilate is literally washing his hands
of the crime. A contemporary touch is added in the last panel where
Christ is shown rising from the dead bearing a Crusader's flag.

*   *   *

The greatest Renaissance artist north of the Alps was Albrecht
Durer. The portrait which is called *Dr. Christoph Scheurl* (page
175), who was a neighbor of the artist, is thought to be by him.
It was customary for well-to-do betrothed couples to have a pair
of portraits painted with the faces turned towards each other. What
this young man's beloved looked like we can only conjecture from
his resigned expression. Whether he is unhappy or not, at least he
is holding a sprig of erygnium in his left hand. This weed was
commonly shown in betrothal pictures because the plant was
supposed to make men irresistable to women. His age, which was
twenty-five, is at the top right next to the year, 1504. Durer was
in the habit of signing all his work "AD" in a characteristic monogram.
In this instance we find only the "A," here woven into the young
man's lace shirt. It has been suggested that the "D" might have been
on the lady's portrait. In that case, however, the pictures would
have to be hung back to back if the initials were to be in the correct
order. Is it possible that the artist, with tongue in cheek, forsaw
little prospect of matrimonial harmony between his clients?

*   *   *

Lucas Cranach the Elder was court painter to three Electors of
Saxony: Frederick the Wise, John the Steadfast and John Frederick
the Magnanimous. In 1508 he was granted a coat of arms. Thereafter
he was in the habit of using the device of a flying snake or dragon
in lieu of a signature. In his *Crucifixion* (page 177) we find it at
the bottom between the lettering and the coat of arms. The date
appears beside the dragon. It looks like 1532, but the last letter
could possibly be a 7. The Art Institute in Chicago owns a larger
and more elaborate version of the Clowes' painting. There the date
seems to be 1533, but once again the last figure is rubbed and could
be an 8. In any case the Indianapolis picture predates the Chicago
one by a year. The inscription at the bottom left reads, "Donated
to the Honorable Heinrich Ranzau, Vicary of the King of Denmark
and Nobleman of Schleswig-Holstein, by Doctor Harwig of Dassel,
in the Emperor's service on October 26, 1596." The coat of arms is
thought to be that of the Dassel family.

Among the biblical characters who are crowded around the Cross are some contemporaries of Cranach. On the white horse, wearing a large ostrich trimmed hat, sits the Elector. Between him and the Cross we see Martin Luther, the ecclesiastical reformer who was a friend of the artist. Cranach also included him again to the right of the right-hand cross. Charles V, the Holy Roman Emperor, sits on the fully armored horse. Finally, just to the right of Christ's feet is a man in an ermine collar, variously identified as a self-portrait or, more likely, as Cardinal Albrecht of Brandenburg.

*   *   *

Henry VIII, the much-married monarch of England, employed Hans Holbein the Younger to be his court painter. Some of the artist's most challenging commissions involved traveling throughout Europe to paint for the King the likeness of princesses who had been proposed for matrimonial consideration. The most celebrated instance involved Anne of Cleves, whose marriage to Henry was being engineered for political reasons. The King, suspicious that she wasn't exactly what he craved, sent Holbein to paint her. "I place more faith in your brush," he told the artist, "than in all the silken words of my ambassadors."

The King's Chancellor, Thomas Cromwell (page 183), sent for Holbein before the artist embarked for Germany. "If you value your head," quoth he, "you had better return with a beguiling portrait." Hardly the most friendly "Bon Voyage!" When Holbein got to Germany his worst suspicions were confirmed. Anne was dull and phlegmatic. She had no conversation but played solitaire by the hour while she noisily munched candies. Not only was she as plain as a pikestaff, but she had been the victim of smallpox which had left her a mass of unsightly scars. Poor Hans was on the horns of a dilemma. There was only one thing in her favor, she loved beautiful clothes and jewels, a characteristic shared by Henry VIII. Consequently, the artist had her dress up in all her finery, painted it all with marvellous attention to detail while he under-played her unfortunate face. The King fell for the portrait and Anne sailed for England. She had a rough crossing and, on arrival, was still miserably sea-sick in her state-room when the impatient King rushed in. So shocked was he by the sight that greeted him that he forgot to leave his gifts. The marriage took place but Anne was immediately pensioned off with a house in the country and a substantial dress allowance. Strangely enough, it was not Holbein but Cromwell who was beheaded.

Though Holbein died of natural causes, he did not enjoy a long life. He died at the age of forty-five or forty-six of a death attributed to the plague. The *Self-Portrait* (page 179) shows him at the end of his life. His initials, age, and date are clearly shown in the background. The painting is the reflection from a convex mirror. While such distortions were used in the middle of the 15th century (see the famous Wedding of Arnolfi by Jan van Eyck, in the National Gallery, London), the trick was still only rarely used. Here the artist has heightened the illusion by painting it on a convex panel.

*   *   *

It is always exciting when a long-standing problem is finally solved; for example, Holbein's *Portrait of an Unknown Lady* (page 181). For years it was thought to be a picture of his wife. There is a well-known authenticated picture of Frau Holbein with her children which shows a certain likeness to the lady in the Clowes Collection, but a pendant portrait to the Clowes' was found in Basle, Switzerland. The Clowes' picture was sent to Basle for examination and a special Holbein exhibition. Without doubt the Swiss picture is of the husband of the Indianapolis lady. Whoever he is, he certainly isn't Holbein but the evidence that they belong together is overwhelming. They face each other, are the same size, have identical blue backgrounds, are done on matching paper with the same water-mark and are both done in the unusual technique of conte-crayon (chalk) with watercolor. As soon as the facts were established, Dr. Clowes offered to buy the Basle painting. Unfortunately, a counter offer was made from Switzerland to acquire the Indianapolis work, resulting in a stalemate.

Hopefully, these brief notes on a number of paintings in the Clowes Collection will contribute something to your enjoyment of the works. Opposite each picture, in capsule form, are various facts which will help those of you who may wish to study the treasures in greater depth.

ITALIAN

BADIA A ISOLA MASTER, School of Duccio

Sienese, fl. ca. 1300-ca. 1320

MADONNA AND CHILD, ca. 1310

tempera on panel, 24 1/2" x 20 1/2"

COLLECTIONS: Count Sighard von Enzenberg, Schloss Tratzberg, Austria;
Dr. G. H. A. Clowes, Indianapolis, Indiana.

EXHIBITIONS: E. and A. Silberman Galleries, New York, December 10 to 28, 1957,
Art of the United Nations, No. 1, illustr. (E. Perkel); John Herron Art Museum,
Indianapolis, Indiana, October 3 to November 1, 1959, *Paintings from the Collection
of George Henry Alexander Clowes,* a memorial exhibition, No. 21, illustr. (David
G. Carter); The Art Gallery, University of Notre Dame, Notre Dame, Indiana, March 11
to April 8, 1962, *A Lenten Exhibition,* No. 14; Indiana University Museum of Art,
Bloomington, Indiana, October 1 to 25, 1962, *Italian and Spanish Paintings from
the Clowes Fund Collection,* No. 1 (Henry R. Hope).

LITERATURE: Catalogues cited above as by Duccio. On September 26, 1935,
Dr. W. Suida in a document gave this work to Duccio. Prof. G. Fiocco attributed this
painting to Duccio in a certificate dated October, 1935; Dr. Oswald Siren in a letter
of November 26, 1935 praised the picture as Duccio. Prior to his publication of the
picture, R. van Marle defined this painting as a late work of the master. Raimond
van Marle, "Two Unknown Paintings by Duccio di Buoninsegna," *Apollo,* October 1936,
pp. 213, 214, figs. III, IV as by Duccio executed in the four or five years prior to
1308. Allen W. Clowes in an unpublished study rejected the attribution to Duccio
while assigning it "close to Duccio." Hilde Weigelt, "Madonna mit Kind von Segna
de Bonaventura," *Pantheon,* XVIII, 1936, p. 258, wherein she conveys the attribution
by her late husband, Curt Weigelt, to Segna, and mentions the Von Engenberg
Collection as the picture's provenance. Dr. Gertrude Coor-Achenbach in an undated
unpublished study in the Clowes archives, *A Further Addition to the Oeuvre of the
Badia a Isola Master,* gave the painting to this pupil of Duccio, and dated the work
around 1310. Enzio Carli, in a discussion with Ian Fraser in 1970, emphasized that
the painting is certainly by a pupil of Duccio. In separate documents both Dr. Mark
Roskill and Ian Fraser support the view that the painting is indeed the work of the
so-called Badia a Isola Master.

GADDI, AGNOLO

Italian, fl. 1369-1396

ST. MARY MAGDALENE IN THE WILDERNESS, ST. BENEDICT, ST. BERNARD OF CLAIRVEAUX, AND ST. CATHERINE OF ALEXANDRIA

tempera on panel, reconstituted polyptych of four panels, each 28 1/2" x 8"

COLLECTIONS: Kaiser Friedrich Museum, Berlin, Germany; Dr. G. H. A. Clowes, Indianapolis, Indiana.

EXHIBITIONS: John Herron Art Museum, Indianapolis, Indiana, October 3 to November 1, 1959, *Paintings from the Collection of George Henry Alexander Clowes,* a memorial exhibition, No. 27, illustr. (David G. Carter); Indiana University Museum of Art, Bloomington, Indiana, October 1 to 25, 1962, *Italian and Spanish Paintings from the Clowes Fund Collection,* No. 2 (Henry R. Hope).

LITERATURE: Catalogues cited above. In a letter of May 10, 1927, Dr. Richard Offner attributed these panels to Agnolo Gaddi. B. Berenson, *Italian Painters of the Renaissance, Florentine School,* 2 vols., Phaidon Press, 1963, I, p. 67. Dr. Mark Roskill, in an undated opinion in the Clowes archives was inclined to give the panels to Gherardo Starnina, and dated the work around 1400. These were side panels of a larger altarpiece similar in form to one by Gaddi in the Mellon Collection.

FRA ANGELICO (Giovanni da Fiesole, also called Fra Beato or de Fra Giovanni)
Italian, ca. 1387-1455

NATIVITY, ca. 1423-1426
tempera on panel, predella panel, 10" x 20"

COLLECTIONS: Possibly painted for the Dominican Cloister of the Compagnia del Tempio, Florence; possibly one of three works seen by Vasari in the Bartolomeo Gondi Collection; Kilenyi, Hungary; Ercole Canessa, New York; American Art Association sale, New York, January 11-13, 1934, No. 537; Dr. G. H. A. Clowes, Indianapolis, Indiana.

EXHIBITIONS: John Herron Art Museum, Indianapolis, Indiana, October 3 to November 1, 1959, *Paintings from the Collection of George Henry Alexander Clowes,* a memorial exhibition, No. 1, illustr. (David G. Carter); The Art Gallery, University of Notre Dame, Notre Dame, Indiana, March 11 to April 8, 1962, *A Lenten Exhibition,* No. 1, illustr.; Indiana University Museum of Art, Bloomington, Indiana, October 1 to 25, 1962, *Italian and Spanish Paintings from the Clowes Collection,* No. 5 (Henry R. Hope).

LITERATURE: Catalogues cited above. In an expertise by Dr. W. Suida, June 25, 1934, the panel was given to Fra Angelico, a view he further confirmed in an undated, unpublished study of this picture in the Clowes archives. This view was followed by Dr. Gustav Glueck in a document of July 7, 1934, and by Dr. Robert Eigenberger in a document of July 19, 1934. In a letter of November 10, 1942, to Dr. Clowes, Dr. Erwin Panofsky compared this picture with one in the Vatican Gallery (illus. in R. van Marle, *The Development of the Italian Schools of Painting,* The Hague, 1935, Vol. IX, p. 187) and gave this work to the School of Lorenzo Monaco. Mr. Ian Fraser noted the close relationship between this panel and the left hand predella panel of the Adoration of the Magi, altarpiece by Gentile da Fabriano, in the Uffizi Gallery, Florence (illus. in H. W. Janson, *History of Art,* New York, 1962, p. 282). The sky and parts of the landscape have been overpainted.

UCCELLO, PAOLO, attributed to
Italian, ca. 1397-1485

PROFILE PORTRAIT OF A YOUNG MAN
tempera on panel, hexadecagon, 22 1/4" in diameter

COLLECTIONS: Emile Gavet, Paris, France, about 1890; E. and A. Silbermann, New York; Dr. G. H. A. Clowes, Indianapolis, Indiana.

EXHIBITIONS: Indiana University Museum of Art, Bloomington, Indiana, October 1 to 25, 1962, *Italian and Spanish Paintings from the Clowes Fund Collection,* No. 6 (Henry R. Hope).

LITERATURE: Catalogue cited above. Given to Uccello by Lionello Venturi in an expertise in the Clowes Fund archives dated June 20, 1941, as "most authentic portrait by Paolo Uccello I know of in this country." Concurring opinions given by Hans Tietze on June 27, 1941, and by W. Suida on September 10, 1941, were followed by a later undated study by Dr. Suida in which he noted close affinities between this painting and Uccello's grisaille frescoes in the Chiostro Verde in S. Maria Novella, Florence (the hair), and drawings on both the Uffizi, Florence, and Albertina, Vienna (the ear). Extensive examinations carried out at the I.M.A. in November 1972 revealed insignificant areas of in-painting in the face, and that the original rectangular poplar panel had been altered to its present shape by both subtraction and addition.

BELLINI, GIOVANNI
Italian, ca. 1430-1516

MADONNA, CHILD, AND ST. JOHN (?), ca. 1500
oil on panel, 30" x 23"; signed b.c., [IOANNES BELL/INUS].

COLLECTIONS: Schatzker Collection, Vienna, Austria; Berlin Art Market, 1932; Dr. G. H. A. Clowes, Indianapolis, Indiana.

EXHIBITIONS: Dallas Museum of Fine Arts, Dallas, Texas, June to November, 1936, *Exhibition of Paintings, Sculpture and Graphic Arts,* Renaissance Gallery, No. 9; John Herron Art Museum, Indianapolis, Indiana, October 3 to November 1, 1959, *Paintings from the Collection of George Henry Alexander Clowes,* a memorial exhibition, No. 4, illustr. (David G. Carter); The Art Gallery, University of Notre Dame, Notre Dame, Indiana, March 11 to April 8, 1962, *A Lenten Exhibition,* No. 5, illustr.; Indiana University Museum of Art, Bloomington, Indiana, October 1 to 25, 1962, *Italian and Spanish Paintings from the Clowes Collection,* No. 18 (Henry R. Hope).

LITERATURE: Catalogues cited above. Wilhelm Suida, "Una Madonna di Giovanni Bellini," extract from *Rivista di Venezia,* Agosto 1935-XIII. Dr. Suida first confirmed this attribution in an expertise of May, 1932, at Baden bei Wien; he compared the painting with the Urbino and Frankfurt versions. On May 16, 1932, Dr. Gustav Glueck stated the picture to be by Bellini and mentioned a dozen replicas. In a document, in the Clowes archives, of June 26, 1932, date-lined Cologne, Dr. Georg Gronau assigned the work to Bellini, pointing out the similarities to his Nos. 156-157-158 and to the copy by Pietro Duja (Gronau p. 190). Prof. Giuseppe Fiocco followed suit in a document dated Padua, September 7, 1932; Dr. M. J. Friedlaender gave it to Bellini on September 10, 1932. In a letter of November 10, 1942, to Dr. Clowes, Dr. Erwin Panofsky stated of the iconography of the picture . . . "I found at least that much, that according to Ripa's *Iconologia* of 1593 water could be represented with a bluish garment, fire with a red one and earth with one embroidered with herbs and leaves. Also, pink signified the 'amor per Dio' (love of God), which makes good sense in regard to the three angels surrounding the head of the Virgin." Note similar cherubim in a picture by Bellini in the Academy, Venice, cf.; R. van Marle, *The Development of the Italian Schools of Painting,* The Hague, 1935, Vol. XVII, p. 293. Bernard Berenson, *The Venetian Schools of Painting,* Vol. I, p. 37, designated it as a close follower of Giovanni Bellini. Dr. F. Heineman classified it as a workshop version of a lost Bellini original of around 1490-95, attributing the central group to Girolamo di Santa Croce, *Giovanni Bellini e i Belliniani,* 2 vols., Venice, 1962, I, p. 30, No. 118 (g) and fig. 241. According to Dr. F. Gibbons, it is probably (like the Urbino version) by Lattanzio da Rimini, working on a design of Bellini's, "Practices in Giovanni Bellini's Workshop," *Pantheon,* 33, 1965, p. 153, No. 5.

BELLINI, GIOVANNI
Italian, ca. 1430-1516

MADONNA AND CHILD
oil on panel, 21" x 16 1/2"

COLLECTIONS: Jules S. Bache, New York; Bache sale, Kende Galleries, New York, April 23, 1945, No. 20; Dr. G. H. A. Clowes, Indianapolis, Indiana.

EXHIBITIONS: John Herron Art Museum, Indianapolis, Indiana, October 3 to November 1, 1959, *Paintings from the Collection of George Henry Alexander Clowes,* a memorial exhibition, No. 5, illustr. (David G. Carter); The Art Gallery, University of Notre Dame, Notre Dame, Indiana, March 11 to April 8, 1962, *A Lenten Exhibition,* No. 4; Indiana University Museum of Art, Bloomington, Indiana, October 1 to 25, 1962, *Italian and Spanish Painting from the Clowes Collection,* No. 17 (Henry R. Hope).

LITERATURE: Catalogues cited above. Prof. Roberto Longhi in a document of May 1928 gave the picture to Bellini and dated it about 1430; Baron D. van Hadeln in a manuscript of November 3, 1928, regarded this picture as that referred to as the lost original in his article in *Zeitschrift fur Bildender Kunst* N.F. XXI, 1909/10, p. 139; Dr. Georg Gronau in a manuscript of September 3, 1928, also gave it to Bellini and regarded it as the finest of all the versions. G. Gronau, *Giovanni Bellini, Klassiker der Kunst,* edit. 1930, p. 212, anm. 127/8 again mentioned the picture as Bellini and as the forerunner of the Bonn painting; Dr. Hans Tietze on June 18, 1945 in an expertise repeated Gronau's views. R. van Marle, *The Development of the Italian Schools of Painting,* Vol. XVII, p. 294, The Hague, 1935, mentioned it as a version and linked it with the Madonna at Duveen's (ex-Salamon Coll.), the picture in the Brady Collection, Manhasset, Long Island (ex-Oldenbourg Coll.) and the work belonging to the Kress Foundation (ex-Wesendonk Coll., loan to Bonn). In a manuscript of June 18, 1945, Dr. W. R. Valentiner stated the painting to be by Bellini, ca. 1480/85. On October 22 of the same year, Dr. W. Suida wrote his agreement with the views previously expressed by Longhi. Prof. Lionello Venturi on December 5, 1945, wrote a concurring expertise. Dr. Erica Tietze-Conrat, "An Unpublished Madonna by Giovanni Bellini and the Problem of Replicas in His Shop" in the *Gazette des Beaux-Arts,* June 1948, pp. 379-382, fig. 1, mentioned again by Dr. Suida in his *Catalogue of the Samuel H. Kress Collection* . . . William Rockhill Nelson Gallery of Arts and Mary Atkins Museum of Fine Arts, Kansas City, 1952, under cat. no. 18; Dr. F. Heineman catalogued the painting as a copy of the Kansas City version, in the style of Vincenzo Catena, *Giovanni Bellini e i Belliniani,* 2 vols., Venice, 1962, I p. 13f., No. 45 (c) and fig. 215. Dr. F. Gibbons in a letter to Dr. Mark Roskill in 1966, compared the painting with the versions in Kansas City and Washington and found it closer to the latter, though with the face of the Virgin more drily painted and the mouth smaller, he was inclined to give the Clowes version to a Bellini follower, to whom the design had been handed over.

BOTTICELLI, SANDRO, Circle of
Italian, ca. 1445-1510

MADONNA AND CHILD WITH ST. JOHN THE BAPTIST, ca. 1490
oil on panel, 33" in diameter.

COLLECTIONS: Prince Tassilo Festetics, former Lord-Marshal of the Emperors of Austria-Hungary; Dr. G. H. A. Clowes, Indianapolis, Indiana.

EXHIBITIONS: John Herron Art Museum, Indianapolis, Indiana, October 3 to November 1, 1959, *Paintings from the Collection of George Henry Alexander Clowes,* a memorial exhibition, No. 23, illustr. (David G. Carter); Indiana University Museum of Art, Bloomington, Indiana, October 1 to 25, 1962, *Italian and Spanish Paintings from the Clowes Collection,* No. 9 (Henry R. Hope).

LITERATURE: Catalogues cited above. In an undated document Raimond van Marle attributed this tondo to Piero di Cosimo (1462-1521); Allen W. Clowes in an unpublished study rejected this attribution while pointing out the affinities of this painting to the style of Piero di Cosimo and to Botticelli. Mr. Clowes dated this tondo about 1490 and observed its closeness to a similar composition in the Nardus Collection, Suresnes. Dr. W. Suida agreed in a similar study with the findings of Mr. Clowes defining the work as "circle of Botticelli." Independently, in a note to Dr. Clowes, Dr. Edward Forbes also placed the painting in the circle of Botticelli and its execution in the 1490's.

PERUGINO (Pietro di Christoforo Vannucci)
Italian, 1446/7-1523

CHRIST ON THE MOUNT OF OLIVES
oil on panel, 19" x 17"

COLLECTIONS: Kilenyi, Hungary; Dr. G. H. A. Clowes, Indianapolis, Indiana.

EXHIBITIONS: John Herron Art Museum, Indianapolis, Indiana, October 3 to November 1, 1959, *Paintings from the Collection of George Henry Alexander Clowes,* a memorial exhibition, No. 43, illustr. (David G. Carter); The Art Gallery, University of Notre Dame, Notre Dame, Indiana, March 11 to April 8, 1962, *A Lenten Exhibition,* No. 38; Indiana University Museum of Art, Bloomington, Indiana, October 1 to 25, 1962, *Italian and Spanish Paintings from the Clowes Fund Collection,* No. 10 (Henry R. Hope).

LITERATURE: Catalogues cited above. Letters in the Clowes archives by Dr. W. Suida of September 21, 1935, and Dr. G. Glueck of November 9, 1935, attribute the painting to Perugino. Dr. Suida further analyzed the picture in an unpublished study in the Clowes archives. Dr. Mark Roskill in a later study compares the painting to one by Giovanni Nicola in the church of San Francesco in Perugia and suggests that this painting might be by a late 16th century follower of Perugino.

NEROCCIO DEI LANDI (Neroccio di Bartolomeo)
Italian, 1447-1500

MADONNA AND CHILD WITH STS. JOHN THE BAPTIST AND MARY MAGDALENE
tempera on panel, 28" x 20 1/8"

COLLECTIONS: Conti Chigi-Saraceni, Siena, Italy; Count Ladislaus Karolyi, Fot Castle, Budapest, Hungary; Dr. G. H. A. Clowes, Indianapolis, Indiana.

EXHIBITIONS: Budapest Museum; New York World's Fair, New York, May to October, 1939, *Masterpieces of Art*, No. 265, illustr. p. 6; California Palace of the Legion of Honor and the H. H. de Young Memorial Museum, San Francisco, California, December 29, 1939 to January 28, 1940, *Seven Centuries of Painting*, No. L-8, illustr. p. 30; John Herron Art Museum, Indianapolis, Indiana, December 24 to 31, 1944, Special Christmas showing; E. and A. Silberman Galleries, New York, October 12 to November 1, 1955, *An Exhibition of Paintings*, No. 7, illustr. p. 19; John Herron Art Museum, Indianapolis, Indiana, October 3 to November 1, 1959, *Paintings from the Collection of George Henry Alexander Clowes*, a memorial exhibition, No. 42, illustr. (David G. Carter); The Art Gallery, University of Notre Dame, Notre Dame, Indiana, March 11 to April 8, 1962, *A Lenten Exhibition*, No. 37, illustr.; Indiana University Museum of Art, Bloomington, Indiana, October 1 to 25, 1962, *Italian and Spanish Paintings from the Clowes Fund Collection*, No. 8 (Henry R. Hope).

LITERATURE: Catalogues cited above. B. Berenson, *The Central Italian Painters of the Renaissance*, New York and London, 1897, p. 157; 2nd ed., 1909, p. 207; E. Jacobsen, *Das Quattrocento in Siena, Studien in der Gemaldegalerie der Akademie*, Strassburg, 1908, p. 83; P. Rossi, "Neroccio di Bartolomeo Landi e la Sua Piu Grande Tavola," *Rassegna d'Arte Senese*, V, 1909, p. 30; M. L. Berenson, "Madonne di Neroccio dei Landi," *Rassegna d'Arte, XIII*, No. 5, May 1913, pp. 73-74, illustr.; L. Dami, "Neroccio di Bartolomeo Landi," *Rassegna d'Arte*, XIII, No. 10, October 1913, p. 164, illustr.; J. A. Crowe and G. B. Cavalcaselle, *A History of Painting in Italy*, ed. L. Douglas and T. Boyenius, 6 vols., London, 1903-14, V, 1914, p. 159, No. 6; C. Chledowski, *Siena*, Berlin, 1923, II, p. 225; P. Schubring, in Thieme-Becker, *Kuenstler-Lexikon*, XXII, Leipzig, 1928, p. 295; B. Berenson, *Italian Pictures of the Renaissance*, Oxford, 1932, p. 389 (Italian ed., 1936, p. 335); R. van Marle, *The Development of the Italian Schools of Painting*, 19 vols., The Hague, 1923-38, XVI, 1937, p. 312; C. Brandi, *Quattrocentisti Senesi*, Milan, 1949, p. 272; G. Coor, *Neroccio de' Landi, 1447-1500*, Princeton, 1961, pp. 98, 102, 103f., 105, 169f. (cat. No. 23), 173, 181 and fig. 87; complimentary letters to previous owner by Prof. H. Tietze, February 12, 1937, and Dr. W. Suida; certificate of Prof. Lionello Venturi.

MAINARDI, SEBASTIANO
Italian, ca. 1460-1513

THE HOLY FAMILY WITH ST. JOHN THE BAPTIST AND AN ANGEL
tempera and oil on panel, tondo, 32" in diameter

COLLECTIONS: Baron Raoul Kuffner, Castle Dioszegh, Czechoslovakia, Mrs. G. H. A. Clowes, Indianapolis, Indiana.

EXHIBITIONS: Allen R. Hite Art Institute, University of Louisville, Louisville, Kentucky, October 11 to 31, 1964, *Italian Painting 1300-1600,* illustr. on cover; Franklin College, Franklin, Indiana, May 2 to 16, 1965, *Italian, Flemish and English Painting 1500-1800 — From the Clowes Fund Collection,* No. 1.

LITERATURE: Catalogues cited above as 15th Century Tuscan. E. Fahy, "The 'Master of the Naumburg Madonna' ", *Fogg Art Museum Acquisitions, 1966-67,* Harvard University, 1963, p. 17, cat. No. 3. Ian Fraser, in an opinion dated October 14, 1972, in the Clowes archives, attributes the painting to Sebastiano Mainardi and dates the work about 1500.

TITIAN (Tiziano Veccelli), attributed to
Italian, 1477 (?)-1576

PORTRAIT OF THE GRAND CHANCELLOR OF VENICE, ANDREA DEI FRANCESCHI, ca. 1550
oil on canvas, 34" x 27"

COLLECTIONS: Major and Mrs. Bono, Florence, Italy; Dr. G. H. A. Clowes, Indianapolis, Indiana.

EXHIBITIONS: John Herron Art Museum, Indianapolis, Indiana, October 3 to November 1, 1959, *Paintings from the Collection of George Henry Alexander Clowes,* a memorial exhibition, No. 55, illustr. (David G. Carter); The Art Gallery, University of Notre Dame, Notre Dame, Indiana, March 11 to April 8, 1962, *A Lenten Exhibition,* No. 47; Indiana University Museum of Art, Bloomington, Indiana, October 1 to 25, 1962, *Italian and Spanish Paintings from the Clowes Fund Collection,* No. 20 (Henry R. Hope).

LITERATURE: Catalogues cited above. *Catalogue of the Paintings and Sculpture given by Edgar B. Whitcomb and Anna S. Whitcomb to the Detroit Institute of Arts,* 1954, p. 107; B. Berenson, *Italian Pictures of the Renaissance, Venetian School,* 2 vols., Phaidon Press, 1957, I, p. 186 (attributed to Titian with a question-mark); Harold E. Wethey, *The Paintings of Titian,* 2 vols., Phaidon Press, 1971, II, p. 164, X-39 (as "Venetian School") illustr. Expertises by Dr. Georg Gronau, August 2, 1928, and Dr. G. Fiocco, August 20, 1928, dated the picture about 1550 and gave it to Titian; Dr. Evelyn Sandberg-Vavala in January, 1935, attributed this version to Titian and dated it in the decade 1540-50, while dating the smaller version in the Whitcomb Collection in Detroit around 1530; Dr. Mark Roskill suggests an attribution to the studio of Titian in a study in the Clowes archives.

LUINI, BERNARDINO
Italian, ca. 1481/2-1532

MADONNA AND CHILD WITH ST. JOHN AND THE LAMB,
ca. 1520
oil on panel, 32" x 23"

COLLECTIONS: Duke Francesco III (Sforza), Milan, Italy; Count Ambrosy Migazzy, Hungary; Dr. G. H. A. Clowes, Indianapolis, Indiana.

EXHIBITIONS: Richmond Art Association, Richmond, Indiana, 1948, *Old Masters from Indiana Collections,* No. 15; Los Angeles County Museum, Los Angeles, California, June to July 1949, *Leonardo da Vinci Exhibition,* No. 56, illustr.; John Herron Art Museum, Indianapolis, Indiana, October 3 to November 1, 1959, *Paintings from the Collection of George Henry Alexander Clowes,* a memorial exhibition, No. 38, illustr. (David G. Carter); The Art Gallery, University of Notre Dame, Notre Dame, Indiana, March 11 to April 8, 1962, *A Lenten Exhibition,* No. 32, illustr.; Indiana University Museum of Art, Bloomington, Indiana, October 1 to 25, 1962, *Italian and Spanish Paintings from the Clowes Collection,* No. 14 (Henry R. Hope).

LITERATURE: Catalogues cited above. Dr. W. R. Valentiner in a document of May 8, 1936, gave this picture to Luini and dated it about 1520. On July 30, 1936, Dr. W. Suida wrote a certificate corroborating the painting as Luini; on August 6, 1936, Dr. Georg Gronau stated his support of the picture as a Luini; on October 24, 1936, Dr. George M. Richter wrote an expertise assigning the work to Luini and considering the quality superior to the other versions. Subsequently, Della Chiesa has expressed the opinion to Dr. Mark Roskill that the Indianapolis version is the best after the Rothschild version. Dr. Mark Roskill considers the painting to be the work of a follower or pupil of Luini. The Sforza coat of arms is painted on the back of the picture.

BECCAFUMI, DOMENICO, attributed to
Italian, ca. 1485-1551

MADONNA AND CHILD WITH ST. JOHN THE BAPTIST AND ST. FRANCIS
center: carved and polychromed wood, 12 1/2" x 8 1/2",
wings: oil on panel, 12 1/2" x 4 1/4" each

COLLECTIONS: Private collection, Siena, Italy; Mrs. G. H. A. Clowes, Indianapolis, Indiana.

EXHIBITIONS: Baltimore Museum of Art, Baltimore, Maryland, January 10 to February 19, 1961, *Bacchiacca and His Friends*, No. 41, illustr.; Indiana University Museum of Art, Bloomington, Indiana, October 1 to 25, 1962, *Italian and Spanish Paintings from the Clowes Collection*, No. 15 (Henry R. Hope).

LITERATURE: Catalogues cited above. In 1960, in an undated manuscript, Mrs. Evelyn Sandberg-Vavala placed the side panels in the oeuvre of Beccafumi, while feeling that the carving of the central panel derives from Jacopo della Quercia. Subsequently, both Mr. John Pope-Hennessy and Dr. Ulrich Middeldorf attributed the carved figures of the central panel to Jacopo della Quercia. The Querciesque-Nerocciesque quality of the carving was noted by G. Coor, *Neroccio de' Landi 1447-1500,* Princeton, 1961, p. 52, No. 168a. Dr. Philip Pouncey (1966) drew attention to the influence of Signorelli in the wings, and was inclined to label them Umbrian School of the late 15th or early 16th century.

FOSCHI (OR TOSCHI), PIER FRANCESCO DI JACOPO
Italian, 1502-1567

ST. PHILIP BENIZZI AND THE GAMBLERS
oil on panel, 5 1/2" x 23"

COLLECTIONS: Chevalier Joseph Toscanelli, Florence, Italy, 1883; Lowengard
Collection, Paris, France; Boehler and Steinmeyer, Lucerne, Switzerland; Julius
H. Haass, Detroit, Michigan; Mrs. Lillian Henkel Haass, Detroit, Michigan; Dr. G. H. A.
Clowes, Indianapolis, Indiana.

EXHIBITIONS: John Herron Art Museum, Indianapolis, Indiana, October 3 to
November 1, 1959, *Paintings from the Collection of George Henry Alexander Clowes,*
a memorial exhibition, No. 52, illustr. (David G. Carter); The Art Gallery, University
of Notre Dame, Notre Dame, Indiana, March 11 to April 8, 1962, *A Lenten Exhibition,*
No. 45; Indiana University Museum of Art, Bloomington, Indiana, October 1 to
25, 1962, *Italian and Spanish Paintings from the Clowes Fund Collection,* No. 11
(Henry R. Hope).

LITERATURE: Catalogues cited above as by Andrea del Sarto. *Catalogue of the
Collection Chevalier Joseph Toscanelli,* Florence, 1883, plate XIX; S. Reinach,
Repertoire des Peintures du Moyen Age et de la Renaissance, 6 vols., Paris 1905-23,
I, 1905, p. 539; S. J. Freedberg, *Andrea del Sarto,* 2 vols., Cambridge, Mass., 1963,
I, p. 221, (as in Haass collection and attributed to Foschi); J. Sherman, *Andrea
del Sarto,* 2 vols., Oxford, 1965, II, p. 200, under cat. No. 8 (not accepted as del
Sarto); A. Pinelli, "Pier Francesco di Jacopo Foschi," *Gazette des Beaux Arts,*
6e. ser., 69, 1967, p. 94, fig. 9, pp. 105f., No. 20 (line 3 there misplaced). In an
unpublished study in the Clowes archives Dr. Mark Roskill places the painting in the
oeuvre of Foschi or Toschi; Ian Fraser in an opinion dated October 27, 1972,
also gives the work to Foschi.

Detail

TINTORETTO, JACOPO, attributed to
Italian, 1518-1594

APOLLO AND THE MUSES
oil on canvas, 21 3/4" x 36 3/4"

COLLECTIONS: Archduke Leopold Wilhelm, 1659; Gemalde Galerie, Vienna, Austria by 1882; Princess Thurn and Taxis, after 1907; Dr. G. H. A. Clowes, Indianapolis, Indiana.

EXHIBITIONS: Toledo Museum of Art, Toledo, Ohio, March 1940, *Four Centuries of Venetian Painting*, No. 56 (H. Tietze); John Herron Art Museum, Indianapolis, Indiana, February 14 to March 28, 1954, *Pontormo to Greco*, No. 57, illustr. (R. O. Parks); John Herron Art Museum, Indianapolis, Indiana, October 3 to November 1, 1959, *Paintings from the Collection of George Henry Alexander Clowes*, a memorial exhibition, No. 54, illustr. (David G. Carter); Indiana University Museum of Art, Bloomington, Indiana, October 1 to 25, 1962, *Italian and Spanish Paintings from the Clowes Fund Collection*, No. 21 (Henry R. Hope).

LITERATURE: Catalogues cited above. *Kunsthistorische Sammlungen des Allerhochsten Kaiserhauses*, Vienna, 1882, No. 463 (1895 cat. ed. and 1907 cat. ed. as No. 241); E. von der Bercken - A. L. Mayer, *Jacopo Tintoretto*, 2 vols., Munich, 1923, I, p. 246; H. Tietze, *Tintoretto*, London, Phaidon Press, 1948, p. 351; B. Berenson, *Italian Pictures of the Renaissance, Venetian School*, 2 vols., London, Phaidon Press, 1957, I, p. 173 (as studio of Tintoretto); C. Garas, "Le Tableau de Tintoret du Musee de Budapest et le Cycle peint pour l'Empereur Rodolphe II," *Bull. du Musee Hongrois des Beaux Arts*, 30, 1967, p. 44, fig. 34. The painting was assigned to Tintoretto by Prof. Lionello Venturi, in a certificate of September 1, 1937, and likewise in an unpublished, undated study by Dr. W. Suida, and tentatively attributed to Palma Giovane (1544-1628) by Dr. Mark Roskill in another unpublished, undated study, in the Clowes archives.

ZUCCHI, JACOPO, attributed to
Italian, ca. 1541-1589/90

PORTRAIT OF A LADY
oil on canvas, 48" x 37 3/4"

COLLECTIONS: Dr. G. H. A. Clowes, Indianapolis, Indiana.

EXHIBITIONS: Franklin College, Franklin, Indiana, May 2 to 16, 1965, *Italian, Flemish and English Painting 1500-1800 — From the Clowes Fund Collection,* No. 4.

LITERATURE: Catalogue cited above, as "School of Bronzino." In a letter dated January 8, 1966 to the Director of the Clowes Fund, Mr. Edmund Pillsbury endorsed the suggestion made by Mr. Phillip Pouncey that this painting may be by Jacopo Zucchi, a pupil of Vasari. Zucchi did portraits in Rome for Ferdinand de Medici, starting in 1572 according to G. Baglione, *Le Vite de Pittori, Scultori, Architetti . . . (1642),* Naples, 1733 ed., p. 42. Unfortunately no portraits by this artist have been identified, so the attribution to Zucchi must remain tentative, based on the resemblance it bears to some of the figures in known paintings by Zucchi such as the Madonna in the *Holy Family* in S. Clemente, Rome, Italy.

LO SCARSELLINO (Ippolito Scarsella)
Italian, 1551-1620

MADONNA AND CHILD WITH ST. JOHN
oil on panel, 6 1/4" x 5"

COLLECTIONS: Mrs. G. H. A. Clowes, Indianapolis, Indiana.

EXHIBITIONS: Indiana University Museum of Art, Bloomington, Indiana, October 1 to 25, 1962, *Italian and Spanish Paintings from the Clowes Fund Collection,* No. 16, (Henry R. Hope); Franklin College, Franklin, Indiana, May 2 to 16, 1965, *Italian, Flemish and English Painting, 1500-1800 — From the Clowes Fund Collection,* No. 6.

LITERATURE: Catalogues cited above as "Milanese School, 16th century." In an opinion dated October 24, 1972, in the Clowes archives, Ian Fraser gives this painting to Lo Scarsellino and compares it to the *Madonna and Child with St. Catherine,* No. 37, in the National Gallery of Parma, Italy.

BASSANO, LEANDRO

Italian, 1557-1622

MAN WITH A GLOVE, ca. 1590-1600

oil on canvas, 29 1/2" x 23"

COLLECTIONS: Dr. G. H. A. Clowes, Indianapolis, Indiana.

EXHIBITIONS: Toledo Museum of Art, Toledo, Ohio, March 1940, *Four Centuries of Venetian Painting,* No. 67, illustr. (H. Tietze); Indiana University Museum of Art, Bloomington, Indiana, October 1 to 25, 1962, *Italian and Spanish Paintings from the Clowes Fund Collection,* No. 19 (Henry R. Hope).

LITERATURE: Catalogues cited above as by Titian. A. Venturi, "Tre Ritratti Inediti di Tiziano," *L'Arte,* 8, 1937, p. 56 and fig. 3; unpublished certificates in the Clowes archives by A. Porcella dated May 12, 1936, G. Fiocco dated May 28, 1936, W. Suida, dated June, 1936, W. R. Valentiner dated September 20, 1936, L. Venturi dated June 5, 1939, and an undated certificate by A. Morassi, all give the painting to Titian. In an undated study Dr. Mark Roskill gives the painting to Leandro Bassano and dates the work in the decade 1590-1600.

CARAVAGGIO, MICHELANGELO MERISI DA
Italian, 1573-1610

SLEEPING CUPID, ca. 1608
oil on canvas, 25 3/4" x 41 1/2"

COLLECTIONS: Private collection, Ireland; Dr. G. H. A. Clowes, Indianapolis, Indiana, 1952.

EXHIBITIONS: John Herron Art Museum, Indianapolis, Indiana, October 3 to November 1, 1959, *Paintings from the Collection of George Henry Alexander Clowes,* a memorial exhibition, No. 13, illustr. (David G. Carter); Indiana University Museum of Art, Bloomington, Indiana, October 1 to 25, 1962, *Italian and Spanish Paintings from the Clowes Collection,* No. 22 (Henry R. Hope); Detroit Institute of Arts, Detroit, Michigan, April 6 to May 9, 1965, *Art in Italy, 1600-1700,* No. 4, illustr. (A. Moir); Wildenstein and Co., New York City, New York, October 29, 1968 to January 4, 1969, *Gods and Heroes — Baroque Images of Antiquity,* No. 3 (E. Williams).

LITERATURE: Catalogues cited above. First given to Caravaggio by Prof. Walter Friedlaender in a manuscript of December, 1948 and again in a manuscript of May, 1950. Dr. Lionello Venturi in an expertise of May 8, 1949, attributed the painting to the master and suggested as the date of execution 1600-05. Walter Friedlaender, *Caravaggio Studies,* Princeton, 1955, "Catalogue Raisonne," p. 212, No. 38B reprod., Plate 54. Dr. Friedlaender suggests that this picture was painted about 1608 for one of the Knights of Malta and that the Pitti Palace version was made to be sent to the Grand Duke of Tuscany. This picture was at one time altered to show a sleeping Christ Child. Caravaggio's motif was adopted by Giovanni da San Giovanni in a fresco, cf. Baldinucci, *Notizie,* IV, pp. 201 ff. In *Le Dossier Caravage,* Paris, 1959, Berne Joffroy denies Friedlaender's attribution of the Clowes' *Sleeping Eros* to Caravaggio, pp. 340-42. Unfortunately, he had not seen the Indianapolis painting. His rejection was based on a black and white photograph. In the Detroit 1965 catalogue, Alfred Moir wrote that "the attribution to Caravaggio (of the Clowes painting) should be made with caution at best." He drew attention to the "rather clumsily painted left foot." Subsequent scientific examination in the I.M.A. conservation laboratories followed by the careful removal of layers of heavy varnish and earlier restorations, has revealed a painting, which is, in the opinion of Ian Fraser, superior in every respect to the Pitti version. Following Dr. Moir's catalogue entry, in an exhibition review, "Seicento at Detroit," *Burl. Magazine,* 107, 1965, pp. 370f., H. Hibbard and M. Lewine suggest that the Indianapolis painting is probably from the circle of Caracciolo, a vague attribution based on a painting of a *Sleeping Cupid* at Hampton Court Palace which is given to Giovanni Battista Caracciolo, called Battistello (Neapolitan school, ca. 1570-1637). Dr. Mark Roskill, in an expertise in the Clowes archives, supports this attribution; Alfred Moir, in *The Italian Followers of Caravaggio,* 2 vols., Cambridge, Mass., 1967, I, p. 212, mentions the Indianapolis painting as an "excellent copy" of the Pitti version. In a manuscript in the Clowes archives, Ian Fraser endorsed the findings of Dr. Friedlaender while pointing out that a dogmatic attribution to an artist with so small an oeuvre as Caravaggio, would be impossible.

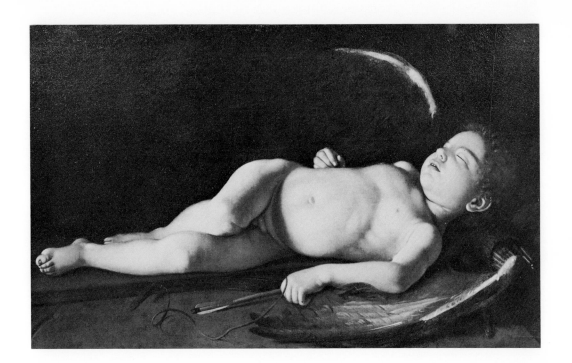

GUARDI, FRANCESCO
Italian, 1712-1793

TWO VENETIAN CANAL SCENES
oil on canvas, each 3 1/2" x 4 1/2"

COLLECTIONS: Mrs. G. H. A. Clowes, Indianapolis, Indiana.

EXHIBITIONS: Indiana University Museum of Art, Bloomington, Indiana, October 1 to 25, 1962, *Italian and Spanish Paintings from the Clowes Fund Collection,* No. 24, (Henry R. Hope); Franklin College, Franklin, Indiana, May 2 to 16, 1965, *Italian, Flemish and English Painting 1500-1800 — From the Clowes Fund Collection,* No. 7.

LITERATURE: Catalogues cited above. Dr. Mark Roskill, in an undated opinion in the Clowes archives assigns the paintings to the "manner of Guardi."

SPANISH

PERE VALL (The Master of the Cardona Pentecost)
Spanish

TWO PAIRS OF SAINTS (Michael and Amador, Stephen and Mary Magdalene), ca. 1400
tempera on panel, each 35 1/2" x 26"

COLLECTIONS: Probably from the Retable of the Pentecost of the Church at Cardona, Spain; Mrs. G. H. A. Clowes, Indianapolis, Indiana.

EXHIBITIONS: John Herron Art Museum, Indianapolis, Indiana, October 9 to November 6, 1960, *Indiana Collects,* Nos. 10 and 11; Indiana University Museum of Art, Bloomington, Indiana, October 1 to 25, 1962, *Italian and Spanish Paintings from the Clowes Fund Collection,* No. 25 (a) and (b) (Henry R. Hope).

LITERATURE: Catalogues cited above. *Archivo Espanol de Arte,* 31, 1958, p. 165, No. 36, illustr. (reproduction of St. Stephen and St. Mary Magdalene).

EL GRECO (Dominico Theotocopuli)
Spanish, 1541-1614

ST. MATTHEW, ca. 1610-1614
oil on canvas, 28 3/8" x 21 7/8", signed m.r. with El Greco's
initials in Greek

COLLECTIONS: Church of Almadrones, near Guadalajara, Spain; Dr. G. H. A. Clowes,
Indianapolis, Indiana, 1952.

EXHIBITIONS: John Herron Art Museum, Indianapolis, Indiana, February 14 to
March 28, 1954, *Pontormo to Greco,* No. 65, illustr. (R. O. Parks); John Herron Art
Museum, Indianapolis, Indiana, October 3 to November 1, 1959, *Paintings from the
Collection of George Henry Alexander Clowes,* a memorial exhibition, No. 32,
illustr. (David G. Carter); The Art Gallery, University of Notre Dame, Notre Dame,
Indiana, March 11 to April 8, 1962, *A Lenten Exhibition,* No. 23, illustr.; Indiana
University Museum of Art, Bloomington, Indiana, October 1 to 25, 1962, *Italian
and Spanish Paintings from the Clowes Fund Collection,* No. 27 (Henry R. Hope);
John Herron Art Museum, Indianapolis, Indiana, February 10 to March 24, 1963,
Museum of Art, Rhode Island School of Design, Providence, Rhode Island, April 19
to May 26, 1963, *El Greco to Goya,* No. 22, illustr.; Crown Hill Cemetery, Indianapolis,
Indiana, September 29, 1963, special showing for 100th anniversary.

LITERATURE: Catalogues cited above. E. Lafuente Ferrari, "El Greco: Some Recent
Discoveries," *Burl. Mag.,* 86-87, 1945, pp. 296, 299; J. Camon Aznar, *Dominico Greco,*
2 vols., Madrid, 1950, II, pp. 981, 1053, 1372, No. 291; Museo del Prado, Madrid,
Catalogo de los Cuadros, 1952 ed., pp. 293, 294, Nos. 2889-2892, and *Catalogo
de las Pinturas,* 1963 ed., pp. 306ff; G. Martin-Mery, *Le Greco,* Bordeaux, 1953, No. 22;
H. E. Wethey, *El Greco and his School,* 2 vols., Princeton, 1962, I, fig. 233, II,
pp. 107f, No. 191; Martin S. Soria, lecture, *Greco's Apostolados,* Frick Symposium,
New York, 1941, explained that El Greco included the four Evangelists according to
Byzantine tradition.

EL GRECO (Dominico Theotocopuli)
Spanish, 1541-1614

ST. SIMON, ca. 1610-1614
oil on canvas, 28 3/8" x 21 7/8", signed m.r. with El Greco's
initials in Greek

COLLECTIONS: Church of Almadrones, near Guadalajara, Spain; Dr. G. H. A. Clowes,
Indianapolis, Indiana, 1952.

EXHIBITIONS: John Herron Art Museum, Indianapolis, Indiana, February 14 to
March 28, 1954, *Pontormo to Greco,* No. 66, illustr. (R. O. Parks); John Herron Art
Museum, Indianapolis, Indiana, October 3 to November 1, 1959, *Paintings from the
Collection of George Henry Alexander Clowes,* a memorial exhibition, No. 33, illustr.
(David G. Carter); The Art Gallery, University of Notre Dame, Notre Dame, Indiana,
March 11 to April 8, 1962, *A Lenten Exhibition,* No. 24; Indiana University Museum
of Art, Bloomington, Indiana, October 1 to 25, 1962, *Italian and Spanish Paintings
from the Clowes Fund Collection,* No. 28, (Henry R. Hope); John Herron Art Museum,
Indianapolis, Indiana, February 10 to March 24, 1963, Museum of Art, Rhode Island
School of Design, Providence, Rhode Island, April 19 to May 26, 1963, *El Greco to
Goya,* No. 23, illustr.

LITERATURE: Catalogues cited above. E. Lafuente Ferrari, "El Greco: Some Recent
Discoveries," *Burl. Mag.,* 86-87, 1945, pp. 296, 299; J. Camon Aznar, *Dominico Greco,*
2 vols., Madrid, 1950, II, pp. 1053, 1372, No. 293; Museo del Prado, Madrid, *Catalogo
de los Cuadros,* 1952 ed., pp. 293, 294, Nos. 2889-2892, and *Catalogo de las Pinturas,*
1963 ed., pp. 306ff; H. E. Wethey, *El Greco and his School,* 2 vols., Princeton,
1962, II, pp. 107f., No. 193. Martin S. Soria, lecture, *Greco's Apostolados,* Frick
Symposium, New York, 1941.

EL GRECO (Dominico Theotocopuli)
Spanish, 1541-1614

ST. LUKE, ST. BARTHOLOMEW or ST. MARK,
ca. 1610-1614
oil on canvas, 28 3/8" x 21 7/8", signed l.l. with El Greco's
initials in Greek

COLLECTIONS: Church of Almadrones, near Guadalajara, Spain; Dr. G. H. A. Clowes,
Indianapolis, Indiana, 1952.

EXHIBITIONS: John Herron Art Museum, Indianapolis, Indiana, February 14 to
March 28, 1954, *Pontormo to Greco,* No. 67, illustr. (R. O. Parks); John Herron Art
Museum, Indianapolis, Indiana, October 3 to November 1, 1959, *Paintings from the
Collection of George Henry Alexander Clowes,* a memorial exhibition, No. 34,
illustr. (David G. Carter); St. Luke the Apostle Church, Indianapolis, Indiana,
October 22, 1961, special showing for Church dedication, illustr. in souvenir; The
Art Gallery, University of Notre Dame, Notre Dame, Indiana, March 11 to April 8,
1962, *A Lenten Exhibition,* No. 25; Indiana University Museum of Art, Bloomington,
Indiana, October 1 to 25, 1962, *Italian and Spanish Paintings from the Clowes Fund
Collection,* No. 29 (Henry R. Hope); John Herron Art Museum, Indianapolis, Indiana,
February 10 to March 24, 1963, Museum of Art, Rhode Island School of Design,
Providence, Rhode Island, April 19 to May 26, 1963, *El Greco to Goya,* No. 24,
illustr.

LITERATURE: Catalogues cited above. E. Lafuente Ferrari, "El Greco: Some Recent
Discoveries," *Burl. Mag.,* 86-87, 1945, pp. 296, 299; E. G. Holt, edit., *Literary Sources
of Art History,* Princeton, 1947, p. 461; J. Camon Aznar, *Dominico Greco,* 2 vols.,
Madrid, 1950, II, p. 1072, No. 289; Museo del Prado, Madrid, *Catalogo de los
Cuadros,* 1952 ed., pp. 293, 294, Nos. 2889-2892, and *Catalogo de las Pinturas,*
1963 ed., pp. 306ff; H. E. Wethey, *El Greco and his School,* 2 vols., Princeton, 1962,
II, pp. 107f., No. 190. Martin S. Soria, lecture, *Greco's Apostolados,* Frick
Symposium, New York, 1941.

EL GRECO (Dominico Theotoçopuli)
Spanish, 1541-1614

CHRIST BEARING THE CROSS
oil on canvas, 8 7/8" x 7 1/8"

COLLECTIONS: Possibly Lois Perez, Alcoy, near Valencia, Spain; Dr. Frank G.
McComber; Dr. G. H. A. Clowes, Indianapolis, Indiana.

EXHIBITIONS: John Herron Art Museum, Indianapolis, Indiana, February 14 to
March 28, 1954, *Pontormo to Greco,* No. 63, illustr. (Robert O. Parks); John Herron
Art Museum, Indianapolis, Indiana, October 3 to November 1, 1959, *Paintings from
the Collection of George Henry Alexander Clowes,* a memorial exhibition, No. 30,
illustr. (David G. Carter); The Art Gallery, University of Notre Dame, Notre Dame,
Indiana, March 11 to April 8, 1962, *A Lenten Exhibition,* No. 22, illustr.; Indiana
University Museum of Art, Bloomington, Indiana, October 1 to 25, 1962, *Italian
and Spanish Paintings from the Clowes Fund Collection,* No. 26 (Henry R. Hope);
The Art Gallery, University of Notre Dame, Notre Dame, Indiana, November 7 to
December 26, 1965, *Masters of the 17th Century;* Museum of Fine Arts, St. Petersburg,
Florida, March 30 to April 13, 1969, a special Easter presentation.

LITERATURE: Catalogues cited above. Ludwig Furst attributed this painting to
El Greco in a letter of November 20, 1944. J. C. Aznar, *Dominico Greco,* 2 vols.,
Madrid, 1950, I, last plate (no cat. no.); H. E. Wethey, *El Greco and his School,*
2 vols., Princeton, 1962, II, p. 175, no. x-45, considered it to be a copy from a
"half-length with cross shown," formerly in the collection of Oscar B. Cintas,
Havana, Cuba, now on loan to the Cummer Gallery of Art, Jacksonville, Florida,
(Wethey, I, fig. 180 and II, p. 41, No. 59).

EL GRECO (Dominico Theotocopuli), School of
Spanish, 1541-1614

ST. JUDAS THADDAEUS OR ST. THOMAS (?)
oil on canvas, 42" x 25 1/2"

COLLECTIONS: Private collection, Madrid, Spain; Max Rothschild, London, England; Dr. G. H. A. Clowes, Indianapolis, Indiana.

EXHIBITIONS: Indiana University Museum of Art, Bloomington, Indiana, October 1 to 25, 1962, *Italian and Spanish Paintings from the Clowes Fund Collection,* No. 30, (Henry R. Hope); Franklin College, Franklin, Indiana, May 2 - 16, 1965, *Italian, Flemish and English Painting 1500-1800 — From the Clowes Fund Collection,* No. 21.

LITERATURE: Catalogues cited above. A. L. Mayer, *El Greco,* Munich, 1926, No. 216 and fig. 37, cites the painting as a workshop repetition of a lost original, belonging to a series of four saints . . . the other three being St. Andrew, St. John the Baptist and St. John the Evangelist. In an expertise dated October 31, 1931, Dr. Robert Eigenberger assigned the painting to the hand of El Greco; concurring opinions given in 1934 by W. Suida, W. R. Valentiner and Gustav Glueck are all in the Clowes archives. J. C. Aznar, *Dominico Greco,* 2 vols., Madrid, 1950, II, p. 1376, No. 390 and fig. 820; H. E. Wethey, *El Greco and his School,* 2 vols., Princeton, 1962, II, p. 245, No. x-394, considered it to be by Luis Tristan (1586 (?) - 1624) or his school, ca. 1620. In an opinion dated September 23, 1972, in the Clowes archives, Ian Fraser rejected the attribution to Luis Tristan or his school and concurred in the view that the painting is "school of El Greco."

RIBERA, JUSEPE DE
Spanish, 1591-1652

ARCHIMEDES, 1637
oil on canvas, 49" x 39", signed l.l. [Jusepe de Ribera, espanol F. 1637]

COLLECTIONS: Fuerstlich Liechtensteinsche Gemaeldegalerie, Vaduz, Liechtenstein; Dr. G. H. A. Clowes, Indianapolis, Indiana.

EXHIBITIONS: Oberlin College, Oberlin, Ohio, winter 1957, *Exhibition of Paintings and Graphics by Jusepe Ribera,* No. 4 (C. Hamilton); John Herron Art Museum, Indianapolis, Indiana, October 3 to November 1, 1959, *Paintings from the Collection of George Henry Alexander Clowes,* a memorial exhibition, No. 49, illustr. (David G. Carter); The Art Gallery, University of Notre Dame, Notre Dame, Indiana, March 11 to April 8, 1962, *A Lenten Exhibition,* No. 42; Indiana University Museum of Art, Bloomington, Indiana, October 1 to 25, 1962, *Italian and Spanish Paintings from the Clowes Fund Collection,* No. 31 (Henry R. Hope); John Herron Art Museum, Indianapolis, Indiana, February 10 to March 24, 1963, Museum of Art, Rhode Island School of Design, Providence, Rhode Island, April 19 to May 26, 1963, *El Greco to Goya,* No. 70, illustr.

LITERATURE: Catalogues cited above. *Descrizione completa di tutto cio che ritrovarsi nella Galleria di pittura e scultura di sua altezza Giuseppe Wenceslas del S. R. I. principe regnante della casa di Liechtenstein (sic.),* Vienna, 1767, p. 105; *Description des tableaux et des pieces de sculpture que renferme La Gallerie de Son Altesse Francois Joseph chef et Prince Regnant de la Maison de Liechtenstein* . . . , Vienna, 1780, pp. 160 and 169; A. L. Mayer, *Jusepe de Ribera,* Leipzig, 1908, p. 188 (1923 ed., p. 201); A. Kronfeld, *Fuhrer durch die furstlich Liechtensteinsche Gemaldegalerie in Wien,* Vienna, 1931, p. 23, cat. no. A57; B. de Pantorba, *Jose de Ribera,* Barcelona, 1946, p. 25; E. H. Turner, "Ribera's Philosophers," *Wadsworth Atheneum Bull.,* Spring, 1958, pp. 5-14, note 5, fig. 2; D. Fitz Darby, "Ribera and the Wise Men," *Art Bull.,* 45, 1962, pp. 298f. and fig. 9.

ZURBARAN, FRANCISCO DE, School of
Spanish, 1598-1664

STONING OF A DOMINICAN MARTYR
oil on canvas, 24 3/4" x 16 3/4"

COLLECTIONS: Mrs. G. H. A. Clowes, Indianapolis, Indiana.

EXHIBITIONS: The Art Gallery, University of Notre Dame, Notre Dame, Indiana, March 11 to April 8, 1962, *A Lenten Exhibition,* No. 51; Indiana University Museum of Art, Bloomington, Indiana, October 1 to 25, 1962, *Italian and Spanish Paintings from the Clowes Collection,* No. 33 (Henry R. Hope).

LITERATURE: Catalogues cited above.

VELAZQUEZ, DIEGO, attributed to
Spanish, 1599-1660

STILL LIFE
oil on canvas, 24 1/2" x 28"

COLLECTIONS: Dr. G. H. A. Clowes, Indianapolis, Indiana.

EXHIBITIONS: John Herron Art Museum, Indianapolis, Indiana, October 3 to
November 1, 1959, *Paintings from the Collection of George Henry Alexander Clowes,*
a memorial exhibition, No. 53, illustr. (David G. Carter); The Art Gallery, University
of Notre Dame, Notre Dame, Indiana, March 11 to April 8, 1962, *A Lenten Exhibition,*
No. 46; Indiana University Museum of Art, Bloomington, Indiana, October 1 to
25, 1962, *Italian and Spanish Paintings from the Clowes Fund Collection,* No. 32,
(Henry R. Hope).

LITERATURE: Catalogues cited above, as "Spanish School." In an undated opinion
in the Clowes archives Dr. Mark Roskill gives the painting to a Spanish or Italian
artist working in the 18th century. Ian Fraser, in a conflicting opinion dated
December 9, 1972, gives the work to Velazquez while noting that the unusual
composition can be accounted for in view of the likelihood that this picture was
once part of the right side of a much larger canvas.

VELAZQUEZ, DIEGO, School of
Spanish, 1599-1660

PORTRAIT OF A LADY
oil on canvas, 21 1/4" x 19 1/4"

COLLECTIONS: Stchoukine Collection, Moscow, Russia; P. Mersch, Paris, France; Dr. G. H. A. Clowes, Indianapolis, Indiana.

EXHIBITIONS: Georges Petit Gallery, Paris, France, May 1909, *Paintings from the Collection of P. Mersch,* No. 96, illustr.; Indiana University Museum of Art, Bloomington, Indiana, October 1 to 25, 1962, *Italian and Spanish Paintings from the Clowes Fund Collection,* No. 34 (Henry R. Hope).

LITERATURE: Catalogues cited above. In an expertise in the Clowes archives, datelined New York, October 20, 1945, Dr. Lopez-Rey attributes this painting to Velazquez and dates the work about 1625-1626. He noted that the canvas had been cut down since 1909, at which time it had measured about 25 1/2" x 21 1/4".

MURILLO, BARTOLOME ESTEBAN
Spanish, 1617-1682

MADONNA IN PRAYER
oil on canvas, 20" x 14 3/4"

COLLECTIONS: Marquess of Lansdowne, Bowood House, Calne, Wiltshire, England;
Elizabeth Holmes Fisher, Los Angeles, California; Private collection, U.S.A., Mrs.
G. H. A. Clowes, Indianapolis, Indiana.

LITERATURE: W. Stirling-Maxwell, *Annals of the Artists of Spain,* 3 vols., London,
1848, III, p. 1420 (1891 ed., IV, p. 1609); E. E. Minor, *Murillo,* London, 1881, p. 75;
C. B. Curtis, *Velazquez and Murillo,* London, 1883, No. 75; A. M. Jameson, *Companion
to the Most Celebrated Private Galleries of Art in London,* London, 1884, p. 306,
No. 31; M. Bryan, *Dictionary of Painters and Engravers,* 2 vols., London, 1889, II,
p. 190 (1904 ed., III, p. 388); A. F. Calvert, *Murillo, A Biography and Appreciation,*
London - New York, 1907, p. 157.

GOYA Y LUCIENTES, FRANCISCO JOSE DE, attributed to
Spanish, 1746-1828

EL JUEGO DE BARRAS
oil on panel, 24 1/2" x 27 1/2"

COLLECTIONS: Dr. G. H. A. Clowes, Indianapolis, Indiana.

EXHIBITIONS: Fort Worth Art Center, Fort Worth, Texas, October 8 to 31, 1954, *Inaugural Exhibition,* No. 37, illustr.; John Herron Art Museum, Indianapolis, Indiana, October 3 to November 1, 1959, *Paintings from the Collection of George Henry Alexander Clowes,* a memorial exhibition, No. 28, illustr. (David G. Carter); The Art Gallery, University of Notre Dame, Notre Dame, Indiana, March 11 to April 8, 1962, *A Lenten Exhibition,* No. 20; Indiana University Museum of Art, Bloomington, Indiana, October 1 to 25, 1962, *Italian and Spanish Paintings from the Clowes Fund Collection,* No. 37 (Henry R. Hope); John Herron Art Museum, Indianapolis, Indiana, February 10 to March 24, 1963, Museum of Art, Rhode Island School of Design, Providence, Rhode Island, April 19 to May 26, 1963, *El Greco to Goya,* No. 31, illustr.; Cummer Gallery of Art, Jacksonville, Florida, October 28 to November 30, 1965, *700 Years of Spanish Art,* No. 46, illustr.

LITERATURE: Catalogues cited above. In an unpublished manuscript of May 3, 1943, Stephan Bourgeois attributed this "Game of Bars" to Goya and the year 1815. Likewise Dr. J. Lopez-Rey in a certificate of September 21, 1944, assigned the painting to Goya and the period 1810-1818. Martin S. Soria, *Catalogue of Spanish Paintings Done Between 1550-1850, in the United States and Canada,* Cambridge, Massachusetts, 1947, p. 384, No. 238, referred to it as "A Fight," about 1860-65, by Eugenio Lucas y Padilla (1824-1870). J. Gudiol, "Paintings by Goya in the Buenos Aires Museum," *Burlington Magazine,* 107, 1965, p. 16. In an opinion in the Clowes archives, Dr. Mark Roskill suggests that the painting may be by Eugenio Lucas de Villamil (1863 (?) - 1918), son of the elder Lucas. X-ray photographs, taken in the I.M.A. laboratories in March 1973, revealed a 15th century Spanish primitive painting, of three saints in a landscape, under the existing painting.

GOYA Y LUCIENTES, FRANCISCO JOSE DE, attributed to
Spanish, 1746-1828

PORTRAIT OF A LITTLE GIRL, ca. 1788
oil on canvas, 26" x 21"

COLLECTIONS: Possibly painted for the Governor of Vizcaya, Spain, Anzoategui, 1788; Don Aniceto Amat, Barcelona, Spain; Don Esteban Esqueu, Havana, Cuba; Mrs. Mercedes Esqueu Reinhardt, New York; Dr. G. H. A. Clowes, Indianapolis, Indiana.

EXHIBITIONS: The Syracuse Museum of Fine Arts, Syracuse, New York, February 3 to 24, 1957, The Atlanta Art Association Galleries, Atlanta, Georgia, March 10 to 25, 1957, *Goya, Zurbaran and Spanish Primitives,* No. 34, illustr., in Addenda, No. 36, illustr., in initial version of the catalogue; John Herron Art Museum, Indianapolis, Indiana, October 3 to November 1, 1959, *Paintings from the Collection of George Henry Alexander Clowes,* a memorial exhibition, no. 29, illustr. (David G. Carter); The Art Gallery, University of Notre Dame, Notre Dame, Indiana, March 11 to April 8, 1962, *A Lenten Exhibition,* No. 20; Indiana University Museum of Art, Bloomington, Indiana, October 1 to 25, 1962, *Italian and Spanish Paintings from the Clowes Fund Collection,* No. 36 (Henry R. Hope).

LITERATURE: Catalogues cited above. In an expertise of June 6, 1947, Dr. Jose Lopez-Rey attributed the work to Goya and dated it 1785-1787; Martin S. Soria, *Esteve y Goya,* Valencia, 1957, p. 90, No. 16, Plate 33, assigned it to Agustin Esteve (1753-1820 or later), as "Unknown Girl," about 1790-1800. The style of the dress would suggest a date in the 1780's.

GOYA Y LUCIENTES, FRANCISCO JOSE DE
Spanish, 1746-1828

HOLY COMMUNION
brown and gray wash on paper, 10 3/32" x 16 1/8"

COLLECTIONS: Dr. G. H. A. Clowes, Indianapolis, Indiana.

EXHIBITIONS: John Herron Art Museum, Indianapolis, Indiana, March 6 to
April 10, 1955, *European Old Master Drawings in Indiana Collections,* No. 62,
illustr. (Robert O. Parks); The Art Gallery, University of Notre Dame, Notre Dame,
Indiana, March 11 to April 8, 1962, *A Lenten Exhibition,* No. 21.

LITERATURE: Catalogues cited above. Jose Lopez-Rey attributed this drawing to
Goya in a certificate dated April 19, 1945, and dated it between 1817 and 1820.
Dr. Mark Roskill, in an undated opinion attributed the work to Eugenio Lucas y Padilla
(1824-1870).

DUTCH

HALS, FRANS
Dutch, 1580/5-1666

SELF-PORTRAIT, ca. 1650
oil on panel, 13 1/2" x 10"

COLLECTIONS: Dresden Gallery, Dresden, Germany; recorded in the Dresden inventory of 1722 as a self-portrait by Frans Hals No. A 191; Dr. G. H. A. Clowes, Indianapolis, Indiana.

EXHIBITIONS: Detroit Institute of Arts, Detroit, Michigan, 1935, *Fifty Paintings by Frans Hals,* No. 49; Gemeente Museum, Haarlem, The Netherlands, 1937, *Frans Hals Tentoonstelling,* No. 98; John Herron Art Museum, Indianapolis, Indiana, February 27 to April 22, 1937, *Dutch Paintings of the 17th Century,* No. 20, illustr. (W. D. Peat); New York World's Fair, New York, May to October 1939, *Masterpieces of Art,* No. 188, p. 90. illustr. plate 67 (W. R. Valentiner); Los Angeles County Museum, Los Angeles, California, November 18 to December 31, 1947, *Frans Hals and Rembrandt,* No. 19, p. 23 (W. R. Valentiner); North Carolina Museum of Art, Raleigh, North Carolina, April 5 to May 17, 1959, *W. R. Valentiner Memorial Exhibition,* No. 67, pp. 120, 121 (J. Byrnes); John Herron Art Museum, Indianapolis, Indiana, October 3 to November 1, 1959, *Paintings from the Collection of George Henry Alexander Clowes,* a memorial exhibition, No. 35, illustr. (David G. Carter); The Art Gallery, University of Notre Dame, Notre Dame, Indiana, March 11 to April 8, 1962, *A Lenten Exhibition,* No. 26, illustr.; Frans Hals Museum, Haarlem, The Netherlands, June 16 to September 30, 1962, *Frans Hals Exhibition,* No. 58, illustr. fig. 62; Indiana University Museum of Art, Bloomington, Indiana, March 18 to April 10, 1963, *Northern European Painting — The Clowes Fund Collection,* No. 36, illustr. (Henry R. Hope).

LITERATURE: Catalogues cited above. *Katalog der Koniglichen Gemaldegalerie zu Dresden,* 1868 ed., p. 214, No. 940 (1880 ed., No. 1020; 1887-1920 eds., No. 1360); W. Bode, *Studien zur Geschichte der Hollandischen Malerei,* Brunswick, 1883, p. 87, n.l.; C. Hofstede de Groot, *A Catalogue Raisonne of the Works of the Most Eminent Dutch Painters of the Seventeenth Century,* tr. E. G. Hawke, 8 vols., London, 1907-27 (also in German), III, 1910, p. 46, No. 148-1; Fr. Reid, *Das Selbstbildnis,* Berlin, 1931, p. 55 (?). W. R. Valentiner, *Art News,* January 12, 1935; E. P. Richardson, *Bulletin,* Detroit Institute of Arts, February 1935, pp. 50 and 59, illustr.; W. R. Valentiner, *Art in America,* June 1935, pp. 85-103, illustr.; W. R. Valentiner, *Frans Hals Paintings in America,* 1936, p. 88, illustr. Dr. Valentiner was the first to give this picture to Hals in a certificate of February 16, 1934; W. Suida wrote his agreement of Dr. Valentiner's view. Dr. Mark Roskill in an opinion in the Clowes archives, inclines to the view that the picture is the best version of a lost original. L. Goldscheider, *Funf Hundert Selbst Portraets,* 1936, No. 162; K. G. Boon, *Het Zelfportret in de Nederlandsche en Vlaamsche Schilderkunst,* Amsterdam, 1947, p. 23; H. van Hall, *Portretten van Nederlandse Beeldende Kunstenaars,* Amsterdam, 1963, p. 125, No. 820.9.

REMBRANDT HARMENSZ. VAN RIJN
Dutch, 1606-1669

SELF PORTRAIT, ca. 1628-29
oil on panel, 17" x 13", signed with Leiden monogram, l.r.
[RHL.]

COLLECTIONS: Pieter Locquet, Amsterdam, The Netherlands, sale September 22, 1783, No. 325; Prince Georges Lubomirski, Lemberg, Poland; Dr. G. H. A. Clowes, Indianapolis, Indiana.

EXHIBITIONS: Stedelijk Museum, Amsterdam, The Netherlands, September 8 to October 31, 1898, *Exhibition of Paintings by Rembrandt on the Occasion of the Inauguration of Queen Wilhelmina,* No. 9; Leiden, The Netherlands, July 15 to September 15, 1906, *Fetes de Rembrandt,* No. 53c; The Metropolitan Museum of Art, New York, New York, The Toledo Museum of Art, Toledo, Ohio, The Art Gallery of Toronto, Toronto, Canada, 1954-1955, *Dutch Paintings, The Golden Age,* p. 60, illustr.; Marion Koogler McNay Art Institute, San Antonio, Texas, October 1956, (no cat.); The North Carolina Museum of Art, Raleigh, North Carolina, November 16 to December 30, 1956, *Rembrandt and His Pupils,* No. 3, illustr. (W. R. Valentiner); John Herron Art Museum, Indianapolis, Indiana, The Fine Arts Gallery, San Diego, California, February - May 1958, *The Young Rembrandt and His Times,* No. 2, illustr. (David G. Carter); John Herron Art Museum, Indianapolis, Indiana, October 3 to November 1, 1959, *Paintings from the Collection of George Henry Alexander Clowes,* a memorial exhibition, No. 47, illustr. (David G. Carter); The Art Gallery, University of Notre Dame, Notre Dame, Indiana, March 11 to April 8, 1962, *A Lenten Exhibition,* No. 39, illustr.; Indiana University Museum of Art, Bloomington, Indiana, March 18 to April 10, 1963, *Northern European Painting — The Clowes Fund Collection,* No. 37 (Henry R. Hope).

LITERATURE: Catalogues cited above. A. Bredius, "Kritische Bemerkungen zur Amsterdamer Rembrandt-Ausstellung," *Zeitschrift fur Bildende Kunst,* NF 10, 1898-99, p. 167; M. Nicolle, "L'Exposition Rembrandt a Amsterdam," *Revue de l'Art,* 2, 1898, pp. 424ff.; C. Hofstede de Groot, *L'Exposition Rembrandt a Amsterdam,* Amsterdam (1899), No. 9; M. Bell, *Rembrandt van Rijn,* London, 1901, p. 118; E. Moes, *Iconographia Batava,* 2 vols., Amsterdam 1897-1905, II, No. 6693.11; W. von Bode - C. Hofstede de Groot, *The Complete Works of Rembrandt,* 8 vols., Paris 1897-1906, VIII, 1906, p. 54, No. 546; F. Schmidt-Degener, "Le Troisieme Centenaire de Rembrandt en Hollande," *Gazette des Beaux Arts,* ze ser., 36, 1906, p. 276; J. Veth, "Rembrandtiana, V, L'Exposition en honneur de Rembrandt a la Halle au Drap de Leyde," *L'Art Flamand,* 6, 1906, p. 88, illustr., (also in trans, *Onze Kunst,* 5, 1906, p. 84); W. R. Valentiner, *Rembrandt, des Meisters Gemalde,* 3rd ed., Stuttgart 1909, pp. 29, 550, 567; A. von Wurzbach, *Niederlandisches Kunstler-Lexikon,* 3 vols., Vienna-Leipzig, 1906-11, II, 1910, p. 401; C. Hofstede de Groot, *A Catalogue Raisonne of the Works of the Most Eminent Dutch Painters of the Seventeenth Century,* tr. E. G. Hawke, (also in German), 8 vols, London, 1907-27, VI, 1916, p. 272, No. 549; D. S. Meldrum, *Rembrandt's Paintings with an Essay on his Life and Work,* London, 1923, p. 20, No. 91; K. Bauch, *Die Kunst des Jungen Rembrandt,* Heidelberg, 1933, p. 209, pl. 207; A. Bredius, *The Paintings of Rembrandt,* Vienna, Phaidon Press, 1936, No. 3, illustr.; P. L. Grigaut, "Rembrandt and his Pupils in North Carolina," *Art Quarterly,* 19, 1956, p. 106; M. Walicki, "Rembrandt w Polsce," *Biuletyn Historii Sztuki,* 18, 1957, p. 334 and pl. 18; James Britton, "Portrait of the Artist as a Young Man," *San Diego and Point Magazine,* May 1958, p. 44, illustr.; A. Bartsch, *Catalogue Raisonne de Toutes les Estampes qui Formaient l'Oeuvre de Rembrandt et de ses Principeaux Imitateurs,* p. 143, No 87; H. van Hall, *Portretten van Nederlandse Beeldende Kunstenaars,* Amsterdam, 1963, No. 1743.6; K. Bauch, *Rembrandt Gemalde,* Berlin, 1966, No. 289.

REMBRANDT HARMENSZ. VAN RIJN, attributed to
Dutch, 1606-1669

PORTRAIT OF AN OLD MAN WITH A TALL FUR-EDGED CAP
oil on panel, 9 3/4" x 7 1/2"

COLLECTIONS: V. H. Crosby, London, England; Mrs. H. H. Hallahan, London, England; Dowdeswell, London, England; Baron Leopold Hirsch, London, England; A private English collector, London, England; Dr. G. H. A. Clowes, Indianapolis, Indiana.

EXHIBITIONS: Grafton Gallery, London, England, 1910, No. 41; Ehrich-Newhouse Galleries, New York, 1935; John Herron Art Museum, Indianapolis, Indiana, February 27 to April 11, 1937, *Dutch Paintings of the Seventeenth Century,* No. 59 (W. D. Peat); John Herron Art Museum, Indianapolis, Indiana, October 3 to November 1, 1959, *Paintings from the Collection of George Henry Alexander Clowes,* a memorial exhibition, No. 46, illustr. (David G. Carter); The Art Gallery, University of Notre Dame, Notre Dame, Indiana, March 11 to April 8, 1962, *A Lenten Exhibition,* No. 40; Indiana University Museum of Art, Bloomington, Indiana, March 18 to April 10, 1963, *Northern European Painting — The Clowes Fund Collection,* No. 38, illustr. (Henry R. Hope).

LITERATURE: Catalogues cited above. W. von Bode — C. Hofstede de Groot, *The Complete Work of Rembrandt,* 8 vols., Paris, 1897-1906, VIII, 1906, p. 136, No. 587, illustr.; W. R. Valentiner, *Rembrandt, des Meisters Gemalde,* 3rd ed., Stuttgart, 1909, p. 436 (1921 ed., p. 127; 1923 ed., p. 125); H. Posse, *Die Gemaldegalerie des Kaiser-Friedrich Museum, vollstandiger beschreibender Katalog . . . ,* 2 vols., Berlin, 1911, II, p. 186, under No. 828J; C. Hofstede de Groot, *A Catalogue Raisonne of the Works of the Most Eminent Dutch Painters of the Seventeenth Century,* tr. E. G. Hawke (also in German), 8 vols., London, 1907-27, VI, 1916, p. 217, No. 400; D. S. Meldrum, *Rembrandt's Paintings with an Essay on his Life and Work,* London, 1923, pp. 179, 199, illustr., p. 354; Museum Dahlem, Berlin, *Verzeichnis der ausgestellten Gemalde des 13 bis 18 Jahrhunderts,* Berlin, 1961, p. 73, under No. 828 I (1964 ed., p. 97). W. Suida, in a certificate, dates the work about 1655; Von Bode, in another certificate, dates it between 1656-1658; C. Hofstede de Groot certified the work as Rembrandt in April, 1929; W. R. Valentiner, in two certificates of October 11, 1940 and June 5, 1951, dates the work about 1650 and 1654 respectively; Dr. Mark Roskill, in an opinion in the Clowes archives, suggests the name of Aert de Gelder (1645-1727) as a possible attribution.

BOSSCHAERT, AMBROSIUS, The Younger
Dutch, 1609-1645

FLOWERS IN A GLASS VASE
oil on panel, 12 1/2" x 9 1/4", signed l.r. [A. Bosschaert].

COLLECTIONS: John Kenneth Danby, England; Dr. G. H. A. Clowes, Indianapolis, Indiana.

EXHIBITIONS: John Herron Art Museum, Indianapolis, Indiana, February 14 to March 23, 1958 and The Fine Arts Gallery, San Diego, California, April 11 to May 18, 1958, *The Young Rambrandt and His Times,* No. 78, illustr. (David G. Carter); John Herron Art Museum, Indianapolis, Indiana, October 3 to November 1, 1959, *Paintings from the Collection of George Henry Alexander Clowes,* a memorial exhibition, No. 8, illustr. (David G. Carter); Indiana University Museum of Art, Bloomington, Indiana, March 18 to April 10, 1963, *Northern European Painting — The Clowes Fund Collection,* No. 39 (Henry R. Hope).

LITERATURE: Catalogues cited above.

ENGLISH

ENGLISH SCHOOL
17th century

PORTRAIT OF A LADY, ca. 1650
oil on canvas, 20" x 16 3/4"

COLLECTIONS: Mrs. G. H. A. Clowes, Indianapolis, Indiana.

EXHIBITIONS: Indiana University Museum of Art, Bloomington, Indiana,
March 18 to April 10, 1963, *Northern European Painting — The Clowes Fund Collection,*
No. 46, (Henry R. Hope).

LITERATURE: Catalogue cited above, where it was attributed to Peter Lely
(1618-1680). In an opinion dated September 17, 1972, in the Clowes archives,
Ian Fraser rejected the attribution to Lely while holding to the view that the painting
is English from the 17th century.

REYNOLDS, SIR JOSHUA, P.R.A.

English, 1723-1792

PORTRAIT OF MRS. THOMAS WATKINSON PAYLER, 1771
oil on canvas, 30" x 25"

COLLECTIONS: Thomas Watkinson Payler, Heden, Kent, England; Egerton Hammond, St. Alban's Court, Nonington, Kent, England; Dr. G. H. A. Clowes, Indianapolis, Indiana.

EXHIBITIONS: John Herron Art Museum, Indianapolis, Indiana, March 8 to April 20, 1941, *Early British Masters,* No. 26, illustr. (W. D. Peat); John Herron Art Museum, Indianapolis, Indiana, October 3 to November 1, 1959, *Paintings from the Collection of George Henry Alexander Clowes,* a memorial exhibition, No. 48, illustr. (David G. Carter); The Art Gallery, University of Notre Dame, Notre Dame, Indiana, March 11 to April 8, 1962, *A Lenten Exhibition,* No. 41; Indiana University Museum of Art, Bloomington, Indiana, March 18 to April 10, 1963, *Northern European Painting — The Clowes Fund Collection,* No. 48 (Henry R. Hope).

LITERATURE: Catalogues cited above. A. Graves - W. V. Cronin, *A History of the Works of Sir Joshua Reynolds,* 2 vols., London, 1899-1901, II, p. 735; E. K. Waterhouse, *Reynolds,* London, 1939, p. 62. Certificate of November 26, 1931 by W. Roberts dates the picture May-June 1771.

REYNOLDS, SIR JOSHUA, School of

English, 1723-1792

PORTRAIT OF MRS. CHARLES JAMES FOX, ca. 1775-80

oil on canvas, 30" x 25"

COLLECTIONS: Dr. G. H. A. Clowes, Indianapolis, Indiana.

EXHIBITIONS: Indiana University Museum of Art, Bloomington, Indiana, March 18 to April 10, 1963, *Northern European Painting — The Clowes Fund Collection,* No. 49 (Henry R. Hope); Franklin College, Franklin, Indiana, May 2 to 16, 1965, *Italian, Flemish and English Painting, 1500-1800 — From the Clowes Fund Collection,* No. 17.

LITERATURE: Catalogues cited above. The portrait was attributed to Sir Joshua Reynolds by Dr. G. Mueller in an opinion dated March 1932, in the Clowes archives; a subsequent opinion by Dr. Mark Roskill suggests a "School of Sir Joshua Reynolds" attribution, and dates the portrait in the late 1770's.

CONSTABLE, JOHN
English, 1776-1837

HARNHAM BRIDGE — SALISBURY, ca. 1821
oil on canvas, 21 1/2" x 30 1/2"

COLLECTIONS: A. P. Fletcher, Oxford, England; Marjorie Fletcher, London, England; Colonel M. H. Brandt, London, England; Dr. G. H. A. Clowes, Indianapolis, Indiana.

EXHIBITIONS: John Nicholson Gallery, New York City, New York, February, 1947, No. 5, illustr.; John Herron Art Museum, Indianapolis, Indiana, October 3 to November 1, 1959, *Paintings from the Collection of George Henry Alexander Clowes,* a memorial exhibition, No. 16, illustr. (David G. Carter); The Art Gallery, University of Notre Dame, Notre Dame, Indiana, March 11 to April 8, 1962, *A Lenten Exhibition,* No. 12; Indiana University Museum of Art, Bloomington, Indiana, March 18 to April 10, 1963, *Northern European Painting — The Clowes Fund Collection,* No. 54, illustr. (Henry R. Hope).

LITERATURE: Catalogues cited above. Margaret Breuning, "This England," *Art Digest,* March 1, 1949, p. 13, illustr. A water-color study of Harnham Bridge, painted 1821, is now in the Victoria and Albert Museum; cf., Sir Charles John Holmes, *Constable and His Influence on Landscape Painting,* illustration facing page 108. In a letter of June 13, 1955, to Dr. Clowes, Dr. W. G. Constable asserted that the picture was certainly by John Constable. In an opinion, based on a photograph, Mr. G. Reynolds verbally rejected the attribution to Constable, while discussing the picture with Dr. Mark Roskill. They both concur in the opinion that it should more properly be attributed to John Dunthorne, Jr. (1798-1832). In a written document of August 23, 1972, in the Clowes archives, Mr. Ian Fraser endorsed the opinion of Dr. Constable, while rejecting the attribution to John Dunthorne, Jr. He noted that the original owner of this picture was a nephew of Mrs. John Constable. Mr. Fletcher was 54 at the time of the artist's death; while he did not collect pictures, it is hardly surprising that one or two canvasses by his distinguished uncle should be in his home.

CONSTABLE, JOHN

English, 1776-1837

THE CORNFIELD, 1826

oil on canvas, 12 1/2" x 8 1/2"

COLLECTIONS: Private collection, London, England; George Eames, Boston, Massachusetts; Dr. G. H. A. Clowes, Indianapolis, Indiana.

EXHIBITIONS: John Herron Art Museum, Indianapolis, Indiana, March 8 to April 20, 1941, *Early British Masters,* No. 3, illustr. (W. D. Peat); John Herron Art Museum, Indianapolis, Indiana, October 3 to November 1, 1959, *Paintings from the Collection of George Henry Alexander Clowes,* a memorial exhibition, No. 15, illustr. (David G. Carter); Indiana University Museum of Art, Bloomington, Indiana, March 18 to April 10, 1963, *Northern European Painting — The Clowes Fund Collection,* No. 55 (Henry R. Hope).

LITERATURE: Catalogues cited above. In a discussion with Dr. Mark Roskill in 1966, Mr. G. Reynolds rejected the attribution to Constable, and suggested instead that this might be a work by W. W. Warren of around 1880. Mr. Ian Fraser, in a manuscript dated August 23, 1973, upholds the attribution to Constable citing *The Cornfield,* National Gallery, London, England, No. 130, for which it would appear to be a study.

FLEMISH

VAN DER WEYDEN, ROGIER , attributed to
Flemish, ca. 1399-1464

PORTRAIT OF A MAN
oil on canvas, 14" x 10"

COLLECTIONS: Countess Vetter von der Lilie, Vienna, Austria; Dr. G. H. A. Clowes, Indianapolis, Indiana.

EXHIBITIONS: John Herron Art Museum, Indianapolis, Indiana, October 3 to November 1, 1959, *Paintings from the Collection of George Henry Alexander Clowes,* a memorial exhibition, No. 56, illustr. (David G. Carter); The Art Gallery, University of Notre Dame, Notre Dame, Indiana, March 11 to April 8, 1962, *A Lenten Exhibition,* No. 50; Indiana University Museum of Art, Bloomington, Indiana, March 18 to April 10, 1963, *Northern European Painting — The Clowes Fund Collection,* No. 17, illustr. (Henry R. Hope).

LITERATURE: Catalogues cited above. Certificates of March 6, 1934, by Dr. Gustav Glueck and Dr. Robert Eigenberger, in the Clowes archives, both attribute this portrait to Rogier van der Weyden and to the decade 1450-60. Claus Virch noted, in March 1973, that "the condition of the picture makes any firm attribution difficult, if not impossible."

BOSCH, HIERONYMUS
Flemish, ca. 1450-1516

ECCE HOMO
oil on panel, 24" x 20 1/2"

COLLECTIONS: A European private collection; Dr. G. H. A. Clowes,
Indianapolis, Indiana, 1940.

EXHIBITIONS: The Detroit Institute of Arts, Detroit, Michigan, April 1 to May 31,
1941, *Masterpieces of Art from European and American Collections, Twenty-Second
Loan Exhibition of Old Masters,* No. 3, "The Mocking of Christ," illustr.; John Herron
Art Museum, Indianapolis, Indiana, October 22 to December 24, 1950, *Holbein and His
Contemporaries,* No. 7 (R. O. Parks); John Herron Art Museum, Indianapolis, Indiana,
October 3 to November 1, 1959, *Paintings from the Collection of George Henry Alexander
Clowes,* a memorial exhibition, No. 6, illustr. (David G. Carter); Musee Communal des
Beaux-Arts, Bruges, Belgium, June 26 to September 11, 1960, *Le Siecle des Primitifs
Flamands,* No. 66, illustr.; The Detroit Institute of Arts, Detroit, Michigan, October to
December, 1960, *Masterpieces of Flemish Art: Van Eyck to Bosch,* No. 56, illustr.; The
Art Gallery, University of Notre Dame, Notre Dame, Indiana, March 11 to April 8, 1962,
A Lenten Exhibition, No. 6, illustr.; Indiana University Museum of Art, Bloomington,
Indiana, March 18 to April 10, 1963, *Northern European Painting — The Clowes Fund
Collection,* No. 18, illustr. (Henry R. Hope).

LITERATURE: Catalogues cited above. Dr. W. R. Valentiner on June 29, 1940,
in an expertise, gave the picture to Bosch; Prof. Charles de Tolnay in a letter of
July 7, 1940, attributed this picture to Bosch and thought the state of
preservation and therefore the effect of its colors superior to the Philadelphia
painting; Mr. David Rosen writing from the Philadelphia Museum of Art regarded
this painting as well as the version in the Johnson Collection as by Bosch, and
neither as a copy. Dr. Hans Tietze in a letter of September 1, 1940, regarded
this picture as by Bosch and superior to the version he published in his *Masterpieces of European Painting in America.* E. P. Richardson, "Augmented Return
Engagement . . . of the Masterpieces of Art from Two World's Fairs", *Art
News,* 40-6, May 1941, p. 17, gave the painting to Bosch and considered it superior
to the Johnson Collection version in Philadelphia. C. de Tolnay, *Hieronymus Bosch,*
1965, Eng. tr., London, 1966, p. 352, cat. No. 12a, p. 104, illustr., described it as
a replica, from the atelier of Bosch, though equal in quality to the Johnson version
and even slightly better preserved. D. Buzzati-M. Cinolli, *L'Opera Completa di Bosch,*
Milan, 1966, under cat. No. 27, illustr., referred to it as a copy from the studio of Bosch.
Jheronimus Bosch, Noordbrabants Museum, 's Hertogenbosch, September to November
1967, under cat. No. 25, designated the picture as not an autograph work but very
close to the original.

BOSCH, HIERONYMUS, School of
Flemish, ca. 1450-1516

TEMPTATION OF ST. ANTHONY
oil on panel, 23 3/4" x 19 1/4"

COLLECTIONS: Private collection, Budapest, Hungary; Dr. G. H. A. Clowes, Indianapolis, Indiana.

EXHIBITIONS: According to Dr. W. R. Valentiner, exhibited in Budapest Museum, Hungary, in 1927; The Denver Art Museum, Chappell House, Denver, Colorado, January 1 to February 15, 1947, *Art of the United Nations,* No. 97 in the exhibition; The Addison Gallery of American Art, Phillips Academy, Andover, Massachusetts, February 19 to March 14, 1954, *Shadow and Substance, The Art Film and its Sources,* No. 7, illustr. (B. Hayes); John Herron Art Museum, Indianapolis, Indiana, October 3 to November 1, 1959, *Paintings from the Collection of George Henry Alexander Clowes,* a memorial exhibition, No. 7, illustr. (David G. Carter); The Art Gallery, University of Notre Dame, Notre Dame, Indiana, March 11 to April 8, 1962, *A Lenten Exhibition,* No. 7, illustr.; Indiana University Museum of Art, Bloomington, Indiana, March 18 to April 10, 1963, *Northern European Painting — The Clowes Fund Collection,* No. 19 (Henry R. Hope); The Denver Art Museum, Denver, Colorado, February 13 to March 27, 1966, *Great Stories in Art,* illustr. in leaflet.

LITERATURE: Catalogues cited above. Dr. W. R. Valentiner on December 20, 1944, stated in a manuscript that this picture was a replica of the central panel of the *Temptation of St. Anthony* in the Lisbon Museum and that he regarded this painting as by the hand of the master. Other versions exist including those in the museums of Sao Paolo, Brazil; Boymans, Rotterdam; Musees Royaux, Brussels; and the Musee Royal des Beaux Arts, Antwerp. The Antwerp work is attributed to Pieter Huys (ca. 1519-1581).

WELLENS DE COCQ, JAN, Circle of
Flemish, fl. ca. 1506-1527

LANDSCAPE WITH HERMIT
oil on panel, 19 1/2" x 10 1/2"

COLLECTIONS: Alfred Strauss (Heiman and Strauss), Los Angeles, California;
Dr. G. H. A. Clowes, Indianapolis, Indiana.

EXHIBITIONS: John Herron Art Museum, Indianapolis, Indiana, October 22 to
December 24, 1950, *Holbein and His Contemporaries,* No. 10, illustr. (R. O. Parks);
John Herron Art Museum, Indianapolis, Indiana, October 3 to November 1, 1959,
Paintings from the Collection of George Henry Alexander Clowes, a memorial
exhibition, No. 11, illustr. (David G. Carter); Indiana University Museum of Art,
Bloomington, Indiana, March 18 to April 10, 1963, *Northern European Painting —
The Clowes Fund Collection,* No. 24 (Henry R. Hope).

LITERATURE: Catalogues cited above as by Pieter Brueghel the Elder. The panel
was given to Pieter Brueghel the Elder in an undated manuscript by Dr. Gustav
Glueck (Clowes archives). In a document of December 30, 1948, Dr. W. R. Valentiner
attributed this picture to Pieter Brueghel the Elder. Gustav Glueck, "Pieter Brueghel
the Elder and the Legend of St. Christopher in Early Flemish Painting," *Art Quarterly,*
XIII, Winter, 1950, pp. 36-47, figs. 1, 2, 3; Gustav Glueck, *Das Grosse Breugel-Werk,*
Vienna, 1951, pp. 37ff, cat. No. 2 and Pl. 2, (English ed., *The Large Breugel Book,*
Vienna, 1952). He considered it to be the left wing of a lost triptych of 1552-53
representing a legend of St. Christopher. Technical examinations and X-rays were
conducted at the Fogg Museum, September, 1966. They revealed that azurite pigment
was used—a color unknown in Europe after the 17th century. The beard around the
edges of the panel showed that it had had an attached frame when it was painted. These
facts would tend to confirm Dr. Glueck's theory that it is from a 16th century triptych.
However, the only remotely comparable work attributed to Pieter Brueghel is a panel
of a *Hermit in a Mountainous Landscape,* inscribed "Bruegel 1568," which was in the
collection of M. W. Frilling (16 1/2 x 19 cms.), sold Galerie Groux, Brussels, March 1-2,
1957. As Dr. Glueck noted, the closest extant work is a detailed painting of the same
legend attributed to Jan Wellens de Cocq, in Baron Bissing's collection in Munich,
Germany. Subsequently, various scholars, including Dr. S. H. Levie and Prof. J. Bruyn
have suggested the name of Jan de Cocq. In a manuscript dated August 18, 1972, in the
Clowes archives, Ian Fraser mentioned the similarities between this panel and the
rear of the right wing of the *Crucifixion Triptych,* (Rijksmuseum, Amsterdam,
Holland, No. 669-B-1), attributed to Jan de Cocq, which is a painting of Hell.
Unfortunately, no paintings have been given to Jan Wellens de Cocq with any degree
of certainty, so that the more conservative "circle of" attribution is used here.

ISENBRANDT, ADRIAEN
Flemish, ?-1551

JOSEPH AND MARY IN BETHLEHEM
oil on panel, 5 1/2" x 3 1/2"

COLLECTIONS: Baron Henri Kervyn de Lettenhove, St. Michel-lez-Bruges, Belgium; The Dawson Collection, Zionsville, Indiana; Mrs. G. H. A. Clowes, Indianapolis, Indiana.

EXHIBITIONS: Sheldon Swope Art Gallery, Terre Haute, Indiana, 1961, *Christmas Story Paintings from the Clowes Fund Collection;* The Art Gallery, University of Notre Dame, Notre Dame, Indiana, March 11 to April 8, 1962, *A Lenten Exhibition,* No. 16; Indiana University Museum of Art, Bloomington, Indiana, March 18 to April 10, 1963, *Northern European Painting — The Clowes Fund Collection,* No. 22, (Henry R. Hope); Franklin College, Franklin, Indiana, May 2 to 16, 1965, *Italian, Flemish and English Painting 1500-1800 — From the Clowes Fund Collection,* No. 15, illustr.

LITERATURE: Catalogues cited above as by Martin Coffermans or Flemish School. In a letter of December 9, 1960, Julius S. Held attributed this picture to Marcellus Coffermans (active in Antwerp 1549-1579) or his daughter. Dr. Mark Roskill, in a concurring opinion, suggested that the work could best be attributed to the circle of Coffermans, and dated it around 1550. In an undated opinion, in the Clowes archives, Ian Fraser rejected the attribution to Coffermans and gave the painting to Adriaen Isenbrandt while noting an inferior version in the Carnegie Institute in Pittsburgh, Pennsylvania.

ISENBRANDT, ADRIAEN
Flemish, ?-1551

THE FLIGHT INTO EGYPT
oil on panel, 5 1/2" x 3 1/2"

COLLECTIONS: Baron Henri Kervyn de Lettenhove, St. Michel-lez-Bruges, Belgium; The Dawson Collection, Zionsville, Indiana; Mrs. G. H. A. Clowes, Indianapolis, Indiana.

EXHIBITIONS: Sheldon Swope Art Gallery, Terre Haute, Indiana, 1961, *Christmas Story Paintings from the Clowes Fund Collection;* The Art Gallery, University of Notre Dame, Notre Dame, Indiana, March 11 to April 8, 1962, *A Lenten Exhibition,* No. 17; Indiana University Museum of Art, Bloomington, Indiana, March 18 to April 10, 1963, *Northern European Painting — The Clowes Fund Collection,* No. 21, (Henry R. Hope); Franklin College, Franklin, Indiana, May 2 to 16, 1965, *Italian, Flemish and English Painting 1500-1800 — From the Clowes Fund Collection,* No. 14, illustr.

LITERATURE: Catalogues cited above as by Martin Coffermans or Flemish School. In a letter of December 9, 1960, Julius S. Held attributed this picture to Marcellus Coffermans (active in Antwerp 1549-1579) or his daughter. Dr. Mark Roskill, in a concurring opinion, suggested that the work could best be attributed to the circle of Coffermans, and dated it around 1550. In an undated opinion, in the Clowes archives, Ian Fraser rejected the attribution to Coffermans and gave the painting to Adriaen Isenbrandt while noting an inferior version in the Carnegie Institute in Pittsburgh, Pennsylvania.

ISENBRANDT, ADRIAEN, follower of
Flemish, first half 16th century

MADONNA AND CHILD IN A LANDSCAPE
oil on panel, 8" x 7"

COLLECTIONS: Dr. G. H. A. Clowes, Indianapolis, Indiana.

EXHIBITIONS: John Herron Art Museum, Indianapolis, Indiana, October 3 to
November 1, 1959, *Paintings from the Collection of George Henry Alexander Clowes,*
a memorial exhibition, No. 39, illustr. (David G. Carter); Indiana University Museum
of Art, Bloomington, Indiana, March 18 to April 10, 1963, *Northern European Painting
— The Clowes Fund Collection,* No. 20, (Henry R. Hope).

LITERATURE: Catalogues cited above as by the Master of the Female Half-Length
Figures. Dr. Gustav Glueck in an expertise of February 11, 1937, attributed this
painting to the later period of the Master of the Female Half-Length Figures
(Franco-Flemish, act. ca. 1510-1530). Dr. W. Suida on March 6, 1937, also gave this
painting to the same hand. Prof. R. Koch in a letter of 1967 to Dr. Mark Roskill
rejected the attribution to the Master of the Female Half-Length Figures, and suggested
that it might be the work of Ambrosius Benson (fl. in Bruges by 1519, died 1550) but
that it is certainly the work of a close follower of Adriaen Isenbrandt.

SOUTH NETHERLANDISH MASTER
middle to late 16th century

HOLY FAMILY WITH AN ANGEL
oil on panel, 5" x 4"

COLLECTIONS: Dr. G. H. A. Clowes, Indianapolis, Indiana.

EXHIBITIONS: Indiana University Museum of Art, Bloomington, Indiana,
March 18 to April 10, 1963, *Northern European Painting — The Clowes Fund
Collection,* No. 23 (Henry R. Hope).

LITERATURE: Catalogue cited above as by Martin Coffermans. Pasted on the back
of the shadow box, in his handwriting, in ink, is Dr. W. R. Valentiner's statement:
"Marcellus Coffermans (?) Late 16th Century W.R.V." In a manuscript dated
August 21, 1972, in the Clowes archives, Ian Fraser rejected the attribution to
Marcellus Coffermans and assigned it to the hand of the unidentified South
Netherlandish Master who painted "The Holy Family," Koninklijk Museum, Antwerp,
Belgium, No. 556.

BRUEGHEL, JAN, The Elder
Flemish, 1568-1625

CANAL SCENE, 1612
oil on panel, 15" x 24", signed and dated l.l. [Brueghel 1612]

COLLECTIONS: Jakob de Wit, Antwerp, Belgium, before 1710; Koniglichen Gemaldegalerie, Dresden, Germany; The Duke of Saxe-Meiningen; Dr. G. H. A. Clowes, Indianapolis, Indiana.

EXHIBITIONS: John Herron Art Museum, Indianapolis, Indiana, October 3 to November 1, 1959, *Paintings from the Collection of George Henry Alexander Clowes,* a memorial exhibition, No. 10, illustr. (David G. Carter); The Art Gallery, University of Notre Dame, Notre Dame, Indiana, March 11 to April 8, 1962, *A Lenten Exhibition,* No. 8; Indiana University Museum of Art, Bloomington, Indiana, March 18 to April 10, 1963, *Northern European Painting — The Clowes Fund Collection,* No. 25 (Henry R. Hope); Musees Royaux des Beaux Arts, Brussels, October 15 to December 12, 1965, *Le Siecle de Rubens,* No. 21, illustr.

LITERATURE: Catalogues cited above. Inventory of the Gemaldegalerie of 1722, No. 708 (This number appears on the painting at the lower right). *Katalog der Koniglichen Gemaldegalerie zu Dresden,* 1880, No. 813; *ibid,* 1884, No. 813; *ibid,* 1887, No. 888; *ibid,* 1912, No. 888; *ibid,* 1920, No. 888. A coarser version exists in the Koninklijk Museum, Antwerp, and two smaller variants are known; one is in the Sutterley Hall Collection, England, the other appeared at Christies, May 14, 1965, lot 90.

BRUEGHEL, JAN, The Elder
Flemish, 1568-1625

SEASCAPE WITH A HIGH CLIFF
oil on copper, 4" x 4 1/2"

COLLECTIONS: Baron Henri Kervyn de Lettenhove, St. Michel-lez-Bruges, Belgium; The Dawson Collection, Zionsville, Indiana; Mrs. G. H. A. Clowes, Indianapolis, Indiana.

EXHIBITIONS: Indiana University Museum of Art, Bloomington, Indiana, March 18 to April 10, 1963, *Northern European Painting — The Clowes Fund Collection,* No. 27 (Henry R. Hope).

LITERATURE: Catalogue cited above. In a memorandum in the Clowes archives, Prof. Julius Held attributed this painting to Jan Brueghel the Elder; in a manuscript dated April 17, 1972, Ian Fraser endorsed this attribution while noting the strong influence of Pieter Brueghel the Elder in the unnatural topography of the cliff, which would indicate a date of ca. 1590-1600 for the work. He further drew attention to a variant in the collection of Lord Hesketh, and another which was in the Leonard Koetser Gallery (*Connoisseur,* March 1966, illustr.; also *Apollo,* March 1966, p. XXIX, illustr.).

VAN DEN BUNDEL, WILLEM, attributed to
Flemish, ca. 1577-1656

A LADY WITH HER RETINUE BESIDE A RIVER
oil on panel, 10 1/2" x 13 1/2"

COLLECTIONS: Baron Henri Kervyn de Lettenhove, St. Michel-lez-Bruges, Belgium; The Dawson Collection, Zionsville, Indiana; Mrs. G. H. A. Clowes, Indianapolis, Indiana.

EXHIBITIONS: Indiana University Museum of Art, Bloomington, Indiana, March 18 to April 10, 1963, *Northern European Painting — The Clowes Fund Collection,* No. 28; (Henry R. Hope).

LITERATURE: Catalogue cited above as attributed to School of Jan Brueghel. In a manuscript of August 17, 1972, in the Clowes archives, Ian Fraser noted closer stylistic similarities between this painting and works attributed to Willem van den Bundel (ca. 1577-1656) than to the works of any of the Brueghel family of painters.

RUBENS, PETER PAUL
Flemish, 1577-1640

TRIUMPHANT ENTRY OF CONSTANTINE INTO ROME, 1620-1622
oil on panel, 19" x 25 1/2"

COLLECTIONS: Probably Louis XIII of France, 1622-23; Saint-Marcel tapestry workshop, Paris, France; Marc de Comans, 1623-?; Francois de la Planche, 1627; probably Henri de Valois, died 1676; Philippe, Duc d'Orleans, Palais Royal, Paris, France, before 1723; Earl of Liverpool, London, England; John Smith, England; Hon. G. J. Vernon, England; Dr. G. H. A. Clowes, Indianapolis, Indiana.

EXHIBITIONS: Orleans Gallery, 125 Pall Mall, London, England, April 1793, No. 61; British Institution, London, England, 1815, No. 121; John Herron Art Museum, Indianapolis, Indiana, October 3 to November 1, 1959, *Paintings from the Collection of George Henry Alexander Clowes,* a memorial exhibition, No. 50, illustr. (David G. Carter); The Art Gallery, University of Notre Dame, Notre Dame, Indiana, March 11 to April 8, 1962, *A Lenten Exhibition,* No. 43, illustr.; Indiana University Museum of Art, Bloomington, Indiana, March 18 to April 10, 1963, *Northern European Painting — The Clowes Fund Collection,* No. 32, illustr. (Henry R. Hope); Philadelphia Museum of Art, Philadelphia, Pennsylvania, October 1 to November 1, 1964, *Constantine The Great, The Tapestries — The Designs,* No. 4a, illustr. (David DuBon).

LITERATURE: Catalogues cited above. (Dubois de Saint-Gelais), *Description des Tableaux du Palais Royal,* Paris 1727, p. 409, No. VI; *Catalogue de Tableaux du Palais Royal, appartenant a le Duc d'Orleans,* Paris 1827, p. 405, No. VI; J. Smith, *Catalogue Raisonne of the Works of the Most Eminent Dutch, Flemish and French Painters,* 9 vols., London, 1829-42, II, 1830, pp. 204f., No. 739; A. von Hasselet, *Histoire de P. P. Rubens,* Brussels 1840, p. 284, No. 583; G. F. Waagen, *Treasures of Art in Great Britain,* 3 vols., London, 1854, II, p. 502, No. 14; A. Michiels, *Catalogue des Tableaux et Dessins de Rubens,* Paris, 1854, p. 21, No. 510; C. Bland, *Le Tresor de la Curiosite,* Paris, 1858, Vol. II, p. 151; M. Rooses, *L'Oeuvre de P. P. Rubens,* 5 vols., Antwerp, 1886-92, III, 1890, p. 213, No. 723; E. Michel, *Rubens, His Life, Work and His Time,* New York, 1899, p. 26, p. 31; A. Graves, *A Century of Loan Exhibitions, 1813-1912,* London, 1913, p. 1159, No. 121. The series, of which this sketch is a part, is recorded as follows: A. von Wurzbach, *Niederlandisches Kunstler-Lexikon,* Vienna and Leipzig, 1910, 2 vols., II, p. 513; A. Rosenberg, *Klassiker der Kunst, Rubens des Meisters Gemalde,* Stuttgart and Leipzig, 1911, p. 478; J. Burckhardt, *Rubens,* Vienna and Leipzig, 1937, p. 101; Thieme-Becker, *Kunstler-Lexikon,* 36 vols., XXIX, p. 142; this picture is more recently recorded in L. van Puyvelde, *The Sketches of Rubens,* London, 1940, p. 28, No. 6; D. DuBon, *Tapestries from the S. H. Kress Collection at the Philadelphia Museum of Art,* Phaidon Press, London, 1964, p. 112, under cat. No. 4, and fig. 60. The picture was engraved by N. Tardieu and Lorieux; V. Schneevogt, *Catalogue des Estampes Gravees d'apres Rubens,* Paris, 1873, p. 219.

RUBENS, PETER PAUL, attributed to
Flemish, 1577-1640

PORTRAIT OF A NOBLEMAN IN ARMOR (Sometimes called "The Duke of Mantua")
oil on panel, 12 1/2" x 9"

COLLECTIONS: Private collection, Vienna, Austria; Mr. F. E. Keeler, Los Angeles, California; Dr. G. H. A. Clowes, Indianapolis, Indiana.

EXHIBITIONS: Detroit Institute of Arts, Detroit, Michigan, February 13 to March 15, 1936, *Sixty Paintings and Some Drawings by Peter Paul Rubens,* No. 18; John Herron Art Museum, Indianapolis, Indiana, February 11 to March 11, 1945, *Portraits, 17th to 19th Centuries, From Indiana Collections,* No. 5; John Herron Art Museum, Indianapolis, Indiana, October 3 to November 1, 1959, *Paintings from the Collection of George Henry Alexander Clowes,* a memorial exhibition, No. 51, illustr. (David G. Carter); The Art Gallery, University of Notre Dame, Notre Dame, Indiana, March 11 to April 8, 1962, *A Lenten Exhibition,* No. 44; Indiana University Museum of Art, Bloomington, Indiana, March 18 to April 10, 1963, *Northern European Painting — The Clowes Fund Collection,* No. 31 (Henry R. Hope).

LITERATURE: Catalogues cited above. J. A. Goris - J. S. Held, *Rubens in America,* New York, 1947, p. 28, No. 10; M. Jaffe, "The Deceased Young Duke of Mantua's Brother," *Burl. Mag.,* 103, 1961, p. 378, no. 22 as a copy of painting in the Putnam Foundation. A. and E. Mongan, *European Paintings in The Timken Art Gallery,* Putnam Foundation, San Diego, California, 1969, p. 117, as a copy. Certificates of April 20, 1928 and October 18, 1934 by W. R. Valentiner refer to the panel as a preliminary study for the portrait in the Henry Goldman Collection (now property of the Putnam Foundation); W. Suida in an undated study in the Clowes archives held this portrait to have been painted for the artist's enjoyment and as a personal record; Dr. Mark Roskill in another undated study quotes a letter from F. Grossmann, in which the latter, judging from a photograph, assigned the painting to a French 18th century hand. In an opinion given by Claus Virch, in March 1973, this painting is a copy after the painting in the Putnam Foundation, San Diego, California.

RUBENS, PETER PAUL, School of
Flemish, 1577-1640

PORTRAIT OF A MAN IN A RUFF
oil on panel, 19" x 14"

COLLECTIONS: Prince Leuchtenberg; Dr. G. H. A. Clowes, Indianapolis, Indiana.

EXHIBITIONS: Detroit Institute of Arts, Detroit, Michigan, February 13 to March 15, 1936, *Sixty Paintings and Some Drawings by Peter Paul Rubens,* No. 22; Franklin College, Franklin, Indiana, May 2 to 16, 1965, *Italian, Flemish and English Painting, 1500-1800 — From the Clowes Fund Collection,* No. 9.

LITERATURE: Catalogues cited above. *Bulletin of the Milwaukee Museum of Art,* Vol. V, No. 6, pp. 3 and 4, illustr.; *The Art Digest,* Vol. X, No. 10, February 1936, cover illustr. An attribution to Rubens dated at Vienna September 10, 1931, by Gustav Glueck is in the Clowes archives.

GOVAERTS, ABRAHAM
Flemish, 1584-1626

REST ON THE FLIGHT INTO EGYPT
oil on panel, 21 1/4" x 31 1/2"

COLLECTIONS: Baron Henri Kervyn de Lettenhove, St. Michel-lez-Bruges, Belgium; The Dawson Collection, Zionsville, Indiana; Mrs. G. H. A. Clowes, Indianapolis, Indiana.

EXHIBITIONS: John Herron Art Museum, Indianapolis, Indiana, October 9 to November 6, 1960, *Indiana Collects,* No. 15, illustr.; The Art Gallery, University of Notre Dame, Notre Dame, Indiana, March 11 to April 8, 1962, *A Lenten Exhibition,* No. 9; Indiana University Museum of Art, Bloomington, Indiana, March 18 to April 10, 1963, *Northern European Painting — The Clowes Fund Collection,* No. 26 (Henry R. Hope); Franklin College, Franklin, Indiana, May 2 to 16, 1965, *Italian, Flemish and English Painting 1500-188 — from the Clowes Fund Collection,* No. 11, illustr.

LITERATURE: Catalogues cited above as by Jan Brueghel the Elder and Hendrik van Balen. In a memorandum of 1960 in the Clowes archives, Dr. Julius Held, while he thought it might possibly be by Jan Brueghel the Younger (1601-1678) was more inclined to give it an earlier date and therefore assigned it to the studio of Jan Brueghel the Elder (1568-1625). He saw no basis for attributing the figures to either Hendrik van Balen (1575-1632) or to Frans Francke II (1581-1642). In a manuscript dated August 5, 1972, Ian Fraser rejected the Jan Brueghel-Van Balen attribution and gave it to Abraham Govaerts (active in Antwerp) a close follower of Jan Brueghel the Elder whose woodland views are heavily indebted to those of Gillis van Coninxloo. He compared the painting to two others by Govaerts, *Un Bosco* (Pinacoteca di Brera, Milan, Italy, No. 665), and *The Rape of Europa,* (Koninklijk Museum, Antwerp, Belgium, No. 903).

THE MASTER OF THE WINTER LANDSCAPES (Gysbrecht Leytens?), attributed to
Flemish, 1586-1656

WINTER LANDSCAPE
oil on panel, 4 1/2" x 7 1/2"

COLLECTIONS: Dr. G. H. A. Clowes, Indianapolis, Indiana.

EXHIBITIONS: John Herron Art Museum, Indianapolis, Indiana, October 3 to November 1, 1959, *Paintings from the Collection of George Henry Alexander Clowes,* a memorial exhibition, No. 40, illustr. (David G. Carter); Indiana University Museum of Art, Bloomington, Indiana, March 18 to April 10, 1963, *Northern European Painting — The Clowes Fund Collection,* No. 29 (Henry R. Hope); Franklin College, Franklin, Indiana, May 2 to 16, 1965, *Italian, Flemish and English Painting 1500-1800 — From the Clowes Fund Collection,* No. 13.

LITERATURE: Catalogues cited above. In a certificate of September 4, 1933, Dr. Ludwig Baldass attributed this painting to the Master of the Winter Landscapes, and dated it about 1600. A technical examination at the Fogg Museum, Winter 1966, revealed that, under magnification, the paint handling did not appear to be 17th century. A complete cleaning and further examination in the I.M.A. Conservation laboratories in 1972 found the painting to be in excellent condition and the paint surface to be no more recent than the 18th century.

VAN DYCK, SIR ANTHONY, attributed to
Flemish, 1599-1641

SELF PORTRAIT
oil on canvas, 24" x 19 3/4"

COLLECTIONS: Colonel Hudson, Pershore, Worcestershire, England; private
collection, Texas; The Clowes Fund, Inc., Indianapolis, Indiana.

LITERATURE: In an unpublished study in the Clowes archives dated June 27,
1958, Dr. Ludwig Burchard assigned the painting to Van Dyck and dated the work
1632-40; in a letter to Dr. Mark Roskill of November 13, 1968, Dr. Jaffe considered
the work a studio adaptation from the self portrait which was formerly in the
Holford collection.

BOUT, PIETER
Flemish, 1658-1719, and
BOUDEWIJNS, ADRIAEN
Flemish, 1644-1711

MARKET DAY
oil on canvas, 10 1/4" x 16 1/2"

COLLECTIONS: Private Collection, Nice, France; Dr. G. H. A. Clowes, Indianapolis, Indiana.

EXHIBITIONS: John Herron Art Museum, Indianapolis, Indiana, October 3 to November 1, 1959, *Paintings from the Collection of George Henry Alexander Clowes,* a memorial exhibition, No. 9, illustr., (David G. Carter); Indiana University Museum of Art, Bloomington, Indiana, March 18 to April 10, 1963, *Northern European Painting — The Clowes Fund Collection,* No. 35, (Henry R. Hope).

LITERATURE: Catalogues cited above.

FRENCH

CLOUET, FRANCOIS
French, ca. 1522-1572

PORTRAIT OF THE MARQUIS FRANCOIS DE SCEPEAUX, MARECHAL DE VIEILLEVILLE (1509-1571), 1566
oil on panel, 12 1/2" x 9 1/4", dated [1566], t.r.

COLLECTIONS: Francois de Scepeaux, Paris, France, 1566; the de Scepeaux family, Paris, France; Jean de Scepeaux; Dr. G. H. A. Clowes, Indianapolis, Indiana, 1950.

EXHIBITIONS: John Herron Art Museum, Indianapolis, Indiana, October 3 to November 1, 1959, *Paintings from the Collection of George Henry Alexander Clowes,* a memorial exhibition, No. 14, illustr. (David G. Carter); The Art Gallery, University of Notre Dame, Notre Dame, Indiana, March 11 to April 8, 1962, *A Lenten Exhibition,* No. 11; Indiana University Museum of Art, Bloomington, Indiana, March 18 to April 10, 1963, *Northern European Painting — The Clowes Fund Collection,* No. 6, illustr. (Henry R. Hope).

LITERATURE: Catalogues cited above. E. Moreau-Nelaton, *Les Clouets et leurs emules,* 3 vols, Paris 1924, I, pp. 76, 82, fig. 26 (drawing, British Museum, London, dated 1566); II, pp. 73, 75; III, p. 129, No. 62, p. 263, No. 49 (painting Musee de Versailles, No. 3220); C. Coidnet, *A Gentleman of the Golden Time,* n.d. In an expertise of November 27, 1950, Dr. Max J. Friedlaender assigned the picture to the hand of Francois Clouet, and Dr. W. R. Valentiner, in a similar manuscript of December 13, 1950, also gave it to Clouet.

CLOUET, FRANCOIS, School of
French, ca. 1522-1572

KING CHARLES IX OF FRANCE (?), ca. 1574
oil on vellum, 6 3/8" x 3 1/2"

COLLECTIONS: Jules Robert Auguste, Paris, France, before 1850; M. Rattier
Collection, London, England, 1859; Duke of Hamilton, Hamilton Palace Collection,
England; W. King, 1882; Capt. Bertram Currie, Dingley Hall, England; F. Kleinberger,
New York, 1929; Dr. G. H. A. Clowes, Indianapolis, Indiana, 1937.

EXHIBITIONS: South Kensington Museum, London, England, June 1862, *Special
Loan Exhibition of Art of Medieval, Renaissance and more Recent Periods,* Nos. 2426-
2431 (one of a set of 6 miniatures as by "Janet"); Indiana University Museum of Art,
Bloomington, Indiana, March 18 to April 10, 1963, *Northern European Painting —
The Clowes Fund Collection,* No. 7 (Henry R. Hope).

LITERATURE: Catalogues cited above. In a document in the Clowes archives Dr. W.
Suida identified the subject as a portrait of King Charles IX (1550-1574), based on a
portrait of Charles IX at the age of 20, in Vienna. Dr. Suida dated the Clowes miniature
1574, at the end of Charles IX brief life and two years after the death of Francois Clouet.

CORNEILLE DE LYON
French, fl. 1533/4-1574

PORTRAIT OF MARIE DE GUISE (formerly thought to be of "Diane de Poitiers"), ca. 1550
oil on panel, 5 1/2" x 4 1/8"

COLLECTIONS: Gagnieres Collection, sold 1718; Duke of Hamilton, Hamilton Palace, England; sold Christie's June 17 - July 20, 1882, No. 1653 (bought by Noseda); J. Seligmann and Son, Paris, France, 1937; Dr. G. H. A. Clowes, Indianapolis, Indiana.

EXHIBITIONS: Palais National des Arts, Paris, France, 1937, *Chefs d'Oeuvre de l'Art Francais,* p. 27, No. 44, illustr. (C. Sterling); John Herron Art Museum, Indianapolis, Indiana, October 22 to December 24, 1950, *Holbein and His Contemporaries,* No. 48, illustr. (R. O. Parks); Carnegie Institute, Pittsburgh, Pennsylvania, October to December, 1951, *French Painting: 1100-1900,* No. 45; John Herron Art Museum, Indianapolis, Indiana, October 3 to November 1, 1959, *Paintings from the Collection of George Henry Alexander Clowes,* a memorial exhibition, No. 17, illustr. (David G. Carter); Indiana University Museum of Art, Bloomington, Indiana, March 18 to April 10, 1963, *Northern European Painting — The Clowes Fund Collection,* No. 3, illustr. (Henry R. Hope); Vassar College Art Gallery, Vassar College, Poughkeepsie, New York, October 16 to November 15, 1964, *Sixteenth Century Paintings from American Collections,* No. 7.

LITERATURE: Catalogues cited above. Dr. W. Suida also confirms this Corneille de Lyon as a portrait of Diane de Poitiers in an undated manuscript in the Clowes archives; Henri Focillon, "Chefs d'Oeuvre de l'Art Francais," *L'Illustration,* Christmas, 1937, illustr.; Jacques Baschet, *Pour Une Renaissance de la Peinture Francaise,* Paris, 1946, p. 14, illustr. (coll. J. Seligmann); Germain Seligmann, *Oh, Fickle Taste, or Objectivity in Art,* Cambridge, 1952, preface by Rene Huyge, p. 119, fig. 55 (p. 121). In an undated manuscript in the Clowes archives Ian Fraser cited a painting in the Scottish National Portrait Gallery, Edinburgh, Scotland to show that this is a portrait of Marie de Guise (1515-1560), wife of James V of Scotland and mother of Mary Queen of Scots, rather than a portrait of Diane de Poitiers.

CORNEILLE DE LYON

French, fl. 1533/4-1574

PORTRAIT OF DUCHESSE DE CHATILLON (?)

oil on panel, 7" x 5 1/2"

COLLECTIONS: Lord Boston, England; D. M. Koetser, New York City, New York; Mary Charlotte Hunter, Beech Hill, Nr. Reading, England; sold Christie's April 29, 1949, No. 25, (bought by Mitchell); Dr. G. H. A. Clowes, Indianapolis, Indiana.

EXHIBITIONS: John Herron Art Museum, Indianapolis, Indiana, October 3 to November 1, 1959, *Paintings from the Collection of George Henry Alexander Clowes,* a memorial exhibition, No. 18, illustr. (David G. Carter); Indiana University Museum of Art, Bloomington, Indiana, March 18 to April 10, 1963, *Northern European Painting — The Clowes Fund Collection,* No. 5, (Henry R. Hope).

LITERATURE: Catalogues cited above. On April 1, 1949, Dr. Max J. Friedlaender certified the picture as a work of Corneille de Lyon.

CORNEILLE DE LYON
French, fl. 1533/4-1574

PORTRAIT OF RENE DU PUY DU FOU, ca. 1550 (?)
oil on panel, 6" x 5 3/8"

COLLECTIONS: Walter Gay, Paris, France, 1904; Jules Strauss, Paris, France;
J. Seligmann and Son, Paris, France, by 1937; Dr. G. H. A. Clowes, Indianapolis,
Indiana.

EXHIBITIONS: *Exposition des primitifs francais au palais du Louvre,* Paris, France,
April to July, 1904, No. 177; Cleveland Museum of Art, Cleveland, Ohio, November 1931;
Exposition de l'art Francais, Bruxelles, Belgium, 1935, No. 925; Palais National des
Arts, Paris, France, 1937, *Chefs d'oeuvre de l'art francais,* No. 49 (C. Sterling); John
Herron Art Museum, Indianapolis, Indiana, October 3 to November 1, 1959, *Paintings
from the Collection of George Henry Alexander Clowes,* a memorial exhibition, No. 19,
illustr. (David G. Carter); Indiana University Museum of Art, Bloomington, Indiana,
March 18 to April 10, 1963, *Northern European Painting — The Clowes Fund Collection,*
No. 4 (Henry R. Hope).

LITERATURE: Catalogues cited above. Waldemar George, *L'Art Francais et
l'Esprit de Suite, Renaissance,* March, 1937, p. 28, illustr.

FRENCH SCHOOL
16th century

ABBESS AT PRAYER
oil on panel, 17 3/4" x 11 3/4"

COLLECTIONS: Dr. G. H. A. Clowes, Indianapolis, Indiana.

EXHIBITIONS: John Herron Art Museum, Indianapolis, Indiana, October 3 to
November 1, 1959, *Paintings from the Collection of George Henry Alexander Clowes,*
a memorial exhibition, No. 26, illustr. (David G. Carter); Indiana University Museum
of Art, Bloomington, Indiana, March 18 to April 10, 1963, *Northern European
Painting — The Clowes Fund Collection,* No. 2, (Henry R. Hope).

LITERATURE: Catalogues cited above.

WATTEAU, JEAN ANTOINE, attributed to
French, 1684-1721

THREE STUDIES OF A SEATED WOMAN: TWO OF A HEAD; ONE OF A HAND WITH A FAN, ca. 1717
red, black and white chalk, 8" x 10 1/2"

COLLECTIONS: E. C. Rodriguez, Paris, France; Dr. G. H. A. Clowes, Indianapolis, Indiana.

EXHIBITIONS: Galleries George Petit, Paris, France, 1931, *Exposition Internationale du Cadre;* The Montreal Museum of Fine Arts, Montreal, Canada, April 27 to May 31, 1950, *The Eighteenth Century Art of France and England,* No. 99; John Herron Art Museum, Indianapolis, Indiana, March 6 to April 10, 1955, *European Old Master Drawings, In Indiana Collections,* No. 50, illustr. (Robert O. Parks); Virginia Museum of Fine Arts, Richmond, Virginia, January 20 to March 5, 1956, *Les Fetes Galantes;* The Art Gallery, University of Notre Dame, Notre Dame, Indiana, March 11 to April 8, 1962, *A Lenten Exhibition,* No. 49; Indiana University Museum of Art, Bloomington, Indiana, March 18 to April 10, 1963, *Northern European Painting — The Clowes Fund Collection,* No. 11 (Henry R. Hope).

LITERATURE: Catalogues cited above. Expertises by L. Reau and Hans Tietze, March 24, 1949, agree with Walter Friedlaender's statement of December 11, 1948, regarding Watteau's authorship. Friedlaender dates the drawing ca. 1717. The drawing is not accepted as a Watteau by Dr. Mark Roskill, who calls it a pastiche after Watteau, in an undated study in the Clowes archives. Claus Virch also views this drawing as a pastiche.

WATTEAU, JEAN ANTOINE, Circle of
French, 1684-1721

FOUR LADIES
red chalk on paper, 5 1/2" x 8"

COLLECTIONS: E. C. Rodriguez, Paris, France; Dr. G. H. A. Clowes, Indianapolis, Indiana.

EXHIBITIONS: Indiana University Museum of Art, Bloomington, Indiana, March 18 to April 10, 1963, *Northern European Painting — The Clowes Fund Collection,* No. 12 (Henry R. Hope).

LITERATURE: Catalogue cited above. In a document of February 2, 1955, in the Clowes archives, Dr. Walter Friedlaender gave the drawing to Watteau. Dr. Mark Roskill, in an undated opinion, noted the similarity to a Watteau drawing of *Three Studies of a Woman,* in the National Museum, Stockholm, and is inclined to view the present work as an early copy after Watteau. Claus Virch noted that this drawing is a reverse of the drawing in Stockholm.

WATTEAU, JEAN ANTOINE, Circle of
French, 1684-1721

THREE STANDING LADIES, FROM THE BACK
red and black chalk, 5 3/4" x 7 7/8" over all (three drawings
mounted together)

COLLECTIONS: Andrew H. Noah, Akron, Ohio; Dr. G. H. A. Clowes, Indianapolis,
Indiana.

EXHIBITIONS: John Herron Art Museum, Indianapolis, Indiana, March 6 to
April 10, 1955, *European Old Master Drawings, In Indiana Collections,* No. 49,
illustr. (Robert O. Parks); Virginia Museum of Fine Arts, Richmond, Virginia,
January 20 to March 5, 1956, *Les Fetes Galantes;* Indiana University Museum of
Art, Bloomington, Indiana, March 18 to April 10, 1963, *Northern European Painting —
The Clowes Fund Collection,* No. 13 (Henry R. Hope).

LITERATURE: Catalogues cited above. In an undated study in the Clowes archives,
Dr. Mark Roskill considered the drawing to be a copy after **Watteau**. **Claus** Virch
agreed with Dr. Roskill's opinion.

ROBERT, HUBERT
French, 1733-1808

LA STATUE
oil on canvas, an overdoor, 26" x 60"

COLLECTIONS: Governor Alvan T. Fuller, Boston, Mass.; Mrs. G. H. A. Clowes, Indianapolis, Indiana.

Detail

ROBERT, HUBERT

French, 1733-1808

ITALIAN GARDEN SCENE, 1768

red chalk drawing on paper, 8 1/2" x 12 1/4", signed l.r.,
[Robert] and dated, [1768]

COLLECTIONS: Probably Charles Gasc, Paris, France, ca. 1850; J. Cotter; Dr.
G. H. A. Clowes, Indianapolis, Indiana.

EXHIBITIONS: John Herron Art Museum, Indianapolis, Indiana, March 6 to April 10,
1955, *European Old Master Drawings, In Indiana Collections,* No. 57, illustr. (Robert
O. Parks); Virginia Museum of Fine Arts, Richmond, Virginia, January 20 to
March 5, 1956, *Les Fetes Galantes;* Vassar College, Poughkeepsie, New York,
May 19 to June 11, 1961, Wildenstein & Co., 19 East 64th St., New York, New
York, June 15 to September 9, 1961, *Vassar College Centennial Loan Exhibition,*
No. 67, illustr.; Indiana University Museum of Art, Bloomington, Indiana, March 18
to April 10, 1963, *Northern European Painting — The Clowes Fund Collection,*
No. 15 (Henry R. Hope).

LITERATURE: Catalogues cited above. F. Lugt, *Les Marques de Collection de Dessins
et des Estampes,* Amsterdam 1921, p. 97, No. 543. Attributed to Circle of Robert
by Dr. Mark Roskill in an unpublished opinion in the Clowes archives.

FRENCH
19th century

FIGURES IN A LANDSCAPE
oil on canvas, 9" x 13"

COLLECTIONS: Dr. G. H. A. Clowes, Indianapolis, Indiana.

LITERATURE: Acquired as an oil sketch by Paul Cezanne (1839-1906). Conservatively assigned to the 19th century French or English Schools by Dr. Mark Roskill in an expertise of 1967.

CASSATT, MARY
American, 1845 - died Paris, France, 1926

MOTHER AND CHILD
pastel on paper, 23" x 17", signed l.l., [Mary Cassatt]

COLLECTIONS: American Art Association, New York City, New York; O'Reilly-Adams and Shumann sale, January 23, 1936 ("property of a Boston private collector"); Victor Spark, 1952; Dr. G. H. A. Clowes, Indianapolis, Indiana.

LITERATURE: Dr. Mark Roskill, in an opinion in the Clowes archives considers this work to be a "pastiche" possibly based on the *Mother and Boy* oil painting in the Metropolitan Museum, New York (Havermeyer Collection). Adelyn D. Breeskin accepts the Clowes picture as an autograph work by Mary Cassatt, *Mary Cassatt, A Catalogue Raisonne of the Oils, Pastels, Watercolors and Drawings,* Smithsonian Institution Press, Washington, D.C., 1970, p. 216, No. 606.

GERMAN

AUSTRIAN OR SWABIAN SCHOOL (?)
early 15th century

PASSION OF JESUS CHRIST, ca. 1400
tempera on panel, reconstituted triptych of twelve panels,
each approximately 14" x 7"

COLLECTIONS: A convent near Bregenz, Austria; an Austrian private collection;
Dr. G. H. A. Clowes, Indianapolis, Indiana.

EXHIBITIONS: John Herron Art Museum, Indianapolis, Indiana, October 3
to November 1, 1959, *Paintings from the Collection of George Henry Alexander
Clowes,* a memorial exhibition, No. 2, illustr. (David G. Carter); The Art Gallery,
University of Notre Dame, Notre Dame, Indiana, March 11 to April 8, 1962,
A Lenten Exhibition, No. 2, illustr.

LITERATURE: Catalogues cited above. In a letter to the Clowes Fund,
Incorporated, of March 22, 1960, Dr. Alfred Stange was inclined to view this
work as German Gothic, or Swabian, from the vicinity of Lake Constance.
In a letter to Mr. Allen W. Clowes, of September 10, 1962, Dr. K. G. Boon saw
more affinities to the Westphalian School rather than the less sophisticated
provincialism of Austrian painting at the turn of the 15th century. Prof. Dr. K.
Bauch, in a letter to Mr. Allen W. Clowes, dated June 26, 1963, favored a
Swabian, rather than an Austrian, attribution.

DURER, ALBRECHT, attributed to
German, 1471-1528

PORTRAIT OF DOCTOR CHRISTOPH SCHEURL, JR. (?), 1504
oil on panel, 17 1/2" x 12", inscribed l.c. [A] (on shirt), dated
u.l. [1504, ALT. 23]

COLLECTIONS: Private collection, Hungary; Dr. G. H. A. Clowes, Indianapolis,
Indiana.

EXHIBITIONS: Dallas Museum of Fine Arts, Dallas, Texas, 1936, *Exhibition of Paintings,
Sculpture and Graphic Arts,* The Gallery of Primitives, No. 12; John Herron Art
Museum, Indianapolis, Indiana, October 22 to December 24, 1950, *Holbein and
His Contemporaries,* No. 24, illustr. (R. O. Parks); John Herron Art Museum,
Indianapolis, Indiana, October 3 to November 1, 1959, *Paintings from the Collection
of George Henry Alexander Clowes,* a memorial exhibition, No. 22, illustr. (David
G. Carter); The Art Gallery, University of Notre Dame, Notre Dame, Indiana, March 11
to April 8, 1962, *A Lenten Exhibition,* No. 15; Indiana University Museum of Art,
Bloomington, Indiana, March 18 to April 10, 1963, *Northern European Painting —
The Clowes Fund Collection,* No. 41, illustr. (Henry R. Hope).

LITERATURE: Catalogues cited above. H. Tietze, *Meisterwerke Europaeischer
Malerei in Amerika,* Vienna, 1936, pp. 338-339, No. 202, illustr.; subsequently
(1938) Dr. Tietze modified his opinion, stressing the lack of parallels in Durer's
work of 1503-05, and seeing the work as more related to the portraiture of Hans
Baldung Grien; G. Glueck, "Ein Neu Gefundenes Werk Albrecht Durers," *Belvedere,*
n.s. 7-8, 1934-36, pp. 117ff., illustr.; H. Tietze and E. Tietze-Conrat, *Kritisches
Verzeichnis der Werke Albrecht Durers,* II, *Der Reife Durer,* Basel and Leipzig, 1937-
1938, part 2, pp. 77-78, 217; Dr. E. Panofsky, *Albrecht Durer,* II, Princeton, 1945,
p. 19, No. 92, ". . . . . somewhat reminiscent of portraits by Hans Baldung Grien."
Prior to the above publications, Dr. G. Glueck on March 28, 1935 and Dr. W. Suida
on March 29, 1935, had issued certificates. The identification of the sitter as
Dr. Christoph Scheurl, Jr., was made by Dr. W. Suida.

CRANACH, LUCAS, The Elder
German, 1482-1553

CRUCIFIXION, 1532

oil on panel, 30" x 21 1/2", signed b.l. with the dragon, and dated 1532.

COLLECTIONS: Doctor Hardwig of Dassel, near Einbeck, Hanover, Germany; Heinrich Rantzau, near Plon, Schleswig-Holstein, 1956; Count Wilezek, Schloss Kreuzenstein, near Vienna, Austria; Dr. G. H. A. Clowes, Indianapolis, Indiana.

EXHIBITIONS: Dallas Museum of Fine Arts, Dallas, Texas, June 6 to November 29, 1936, *Exhibition of Paintings, Sculpture and Graphic Art,* No. 15; John Herron Art Museum, Indianapolis, Indiana, October 22 to December 24, 1950, *Holbein and His Contemporaries,* No. 19, illustr. (R. O. Parks); John Herron Art Museum, Indianapolis, Indiana, October 3 to November 1, 1959, *Paintings from the Collection of George Henry Alexander Clowes,* a memorial exhibition, No. 20, illustr. (David G. Carter); The Art Gallery, University of Notre Dame, Notre Dame, Indiana, March 11 to April 8, 1962, *A Lenten Exhibition,* No. 13, illustr.; Indiana University Museum of Art, Bloomington, Indiana, March 18 to April 10, 1963, *Northern European Painting – The Clowes Fund Collection,* No. 42, illustr. (Henry R. Hope).

LITERATURE: Catalogues cited above. Dr. Max J. Friedlaender, in a letter of April 27, 1934, confirms the picture as a work of the Master of 1532; on October 20, 1935, Dr. W. Suida also read the date of this Cranach as 1532 and noted the date of its donation 1596; a document of November 25, 1935, by Gustav Glueck again confirms the earlier notations; Dr. W. R. Valentiner was the last to write an expertise asserting the same facts on December 27, 1935. Daniel C. Rich, *Catalogue of the Charles H. and Mary E. S. Worcester Collection of Paintings, Sculpture and Drawings,* Chicago, 1938, p. 39., mentions the Clowes painting in relation to the same subject in the Worcester Collection, which is dated a year later.

HOLBEIN, HANS, The Younger
German, 1497/8-1543

SELF PORTRAIT, 1542
oil on panel, 4 5/8" in diameter, monogrammed on background on each side of the head [HH] and inscribed [AN. 1542; AETA 45]. Engraved by Vonterman and W. Hollar.

COLLECTIONS: Von Stackelberg family, Schloss Fahna, near Riga, Latvia; Emil Paravicini-Engel, Basel, Switzerland; Dr. G. H. A. Clowes, Indianapolis, Indiana.

EXHIBITIONS: Golden Gate International Exposition, San Francisco, 1939, *Masterworks of Five Centuries,* No. 12a; John Herron Art Museum, Indianapolis, Indiana, October 22 to December 24, 1950, *Holbein and his Contemporaries,* No. 38 (R. O. Parks); E. and A. Silberman Galleries, New York, December 10 to 28, 1957, *Art Unites Nations,* No. 10, illustr. (E. Perkel); John Herron Art Museum, Indianapolis, Indiana, October 3 to November 1, 1959, *Paintings from the Collection of George Henry Alexander Clowes,* a memorial exhibition, No. 36, illustr. (David G. Carter); The Art Gallery, University of Notre Dame, Notre Dame, Indiana, March 11 to April 8, 1962, *A Lenten Exhibition,* No. 28, illustr.; Indiana University Museum of Art, Bloomington, Indiana, March 18 to April 10, 1963, *Northern European Painting — The Clowes Fund Collection,* No. 45, illustr., (Henry R. Hope).

LITERATURE: Catalogues cited above. H. Wormann, "Hans Holbeins d.j. Selbstportrat von Schloss Fahna," *Zeitschrift fur Bildende Kunst,* 10, 1875, pp. 315ff.; A. Woltmann, *Holbein und Seine Zeit,* 2nd ed., 2 vols., Leipzig, 1874-76, I, p. 101, No. I and II, pp. 165f.; H. Knackfass, *Holbein der Jungere,* 4th ed., Bielefeld-Leipzig, 1902, p. 154; P. Ganz, "Das Bildnis Hans Holbeins d.j.," *Jahrbuch fur Kunst und Kunstpflege in der Schweiz,* 5, 1928-29, pp. 287f. and pl. 1; H. A. Schmid, "Wie hat Hans Holbein d.j. ausgesehen," *Anzeiger fur Schweizerische Altertumskunde,* 33, 1931, p. 282 and pl. 19. Expertises in the Clowes archives by P. Ganz, July 24, 1936 and by W. Suida. P. Ganz, "Holbein's Last Self-Portrait," *Burl. Mag.,* 71, 1937, pp. 62ff., illustr.; H. A. Schmid, *Hans Holbein der Jungere,* 3 vols., Basle, 1945-1948, I, p. 19 and II, p. 380; P. Ganz, *Hans Holbein, die Gemalde,* Basle, 1950, p. 240, No. 130, illustr. (English ed., 1950, p. 257); H. A. Schmid, "Ein unbekanntes Selbstbildnis Hans Holbeins des Jungeren," *Das Werk,* 38, 1951, pp. 27ff., illustr.; F. Grossmann, "Holbein Studies—II," *Burl. Mag.,* 93, 1951, pp. 113f.; Hans Waezoldt, "Hans Holbein d.j.," *Taunus,* 1958, frontispiece. Dr. Mark Roskill, in an opinion in the Clowes archives, assigned the painting to a later sixteenth century hand.

HOLBEIN, HANS, The Younger
German, 1497/8-1543

PORTRAIT OF AN UNKNOWN LADY, ca. 1538 (sometimes called "Frau Holbein")
black and colored chalk and watercolor on red tinted paper, 14 1/2" x 11 3/4", signed l.r. [HH.]

COLLECTIONS: Count Hans Wilczek, Schloss Kreuzenstein, near Vienna, Austria; Dr. G. H. A. Clowes, Indianapolis, Indiana.

EXHIBITIONS: John Herron Art Museum, Indianapolis, Indiana, October 22 to December 14, 1950, *Holbein and His Contemporaries,* No. 37, illustr. (R. O. Parks); John Herron Art Museum, Indianapolis, Indiana, March 6 to April 10, 1955, *European Old Master Drawings in Indiana Collections,* No. 2, illustr.; Kunstmuseum, Basel, Switzerland, June 3 to September 25, 1960, *Die Malerfamilie Holbein in Basel,* No. 322, illustr. plate No. 64; The Art Gallery, University of Notre Dame, Notre Dame, Indiana, March 11 to April 8, 1962, *A Lenten Exhibition,* No. 29; Indiana University Museum of Art, Bloomington, Indiana, March 18 to April 10, 1963, *Northern European Painting — The Clowes Fund Collection,* No. 43 (Henry R. Hope).

LITERATURE: Catalogues cited above. P. Ganz, *Les Dessins de Hans Holbein le Jeune, Catalogue Raisonne,* Geneva, 1939, p. 139, No. 464, illustr.; *ibid., Hand-Zeichnungen Hans Holbein des Jungere in Auswahl,* Basel, 1943, p. 36, No. 29, illustr.; H. A. Schmid, *Hans Holbein der Jungere,* 3 vols., Basel, 1945-48, III (Tafelband), 1945, p. 36, No. 118, illustr. and I, 1948, p. 20; *World's Masters New Series, Holbein,* Studio Publications, London and New York, 1948, illustr. plate XXXVIII.

HOLBEIN, HANS, The Younger, attributed to
German, 1497/8-1543

PORTRAIT OF LORD CHANCELLOR THOMAS CROMWELL
oil on panel, 20" x 17"

COLLECTIONS: Charles Penruddocke, 1890; Capt. G. W. Penruddocke; Dr. G. H. A. Clowes, Indianapolis, Indiana.

EXHIBITIONS: New Gallery London, England, 1890, *Exhibition of the Royal House of Tudor,* No. 162; John Herron Art Museum, Indianapolis, Indiana, October 22 to December 24, 1950, *Holbein and His Contemporaries,* No. 36 (R. O. Parks); John Herron Art Museum, Indianapolis, Indiana, October 3 to November 1, 1959, *Paintings from the Collection of George Henry Alexander Clowes,* a memorial exhibition, No. 37, illustr. (David G. Carter); The Art Gallery, University of Notre Dame, Notre Dame, Indiana, March 11 to April 8, 1962, *A Lenten Exhibition,* No. 30; Indiana University Museum of Art, Bloomington, Indiana, March 18 to April 10, 1963, *Northern European Painting — The Clowes Fund Collection,* No. 44.

LITERATURE: Catalogues cited above. A. R. Chamberlain, *Hans Holbein the Younger,* 2 vols., London, 1913, II, p. 61, not accepted as an autograph work; P. Ganz, *Hans Holbein, die Gemalde,* Basel, 1950, p. 234, cat. No. 99 and fig. 29 (English ed., 1950, pp. 249f. and fig. 28), certified as an autograph work. R. Strong, "Holbein in England, I and II," *Burl. Mag.,* 109, 1967, pp. 276ff., as a derivation from a lost original of ca. 1533-34; *The Frick Collection, An Illustrated Catalogue,* 2 vols., New York, 1968, I, p. 236.

OBJECTS

OBJECTS IN THE CLOWES COLLECTION

ROYAL MINTON EARLY MORNING TEA SET. A tea pot and cover, a sugar basin and cover, a pear shaped milk jug, two cups and saucers and an oval two-handled tray. Each piece is decorated with painted flower sprays within royal blue borders enriched with gilding and embellished with the Coronet and Monogram of Her Royal Highness Victoria Alexandra Alice Mary, The Princess Royal of England (1897-1965).

IVORY PLAQUE. French, 15th century. Left wing of a small altarpiece, representing the Madonna and Christ Child flanked by two angels bearing chalices.

IVORY TRIPTYCH. Spanish primitive. The central panel depicts the Madonna and Christ Child flanked by two angels under a canopy. Each wing contains a crowned saint under a canopy. A small predella panel consists of two angels bearing heraldic devices.

MARRIAGE CHEST. Italian, Florentine, 15th century. Low relief carving on the front represents the Adoration of the Magi. Traces of the original polychroming remain.

TERRA COTTA HIGH RELIEF PLAQUE. Italian, Florentine, ca. 1450. Close to the style of Rossellino, the subject is the Annunciation. Small traces of polychrome remain.

TERRA COTTA TOMB HORSE. Chinese, T'ang Dynasty (618-907).

PAIR OF HALL CHAIRS OF CARVED OAK WITH SANED SEATS AND BACKS. English, Charles II, ca. 1665.

TAPESTRY. French Medieval. 50" x 64". This "mille fleurs" tapestry has the Salvator Mundi within a Mandorla in the middle.

RUG. Persian silk. 13'6" x 10'.

PAIR OF BATHSTONE RAMPANT LIONS WITH SHIELDS. English.

ALPHABETICAL INDEX OF ARTISTS

FRA ANGELICO, Nativity 8
AUSTRIAN OR SWABIAN SCHOOL (?), Passion of Jesus Christ 172

BADIA A ISOLA MASTER, Madonna and Child 2
BASSANO, LEANDRO, Man with a Glove 40
BECCAFUMl, DOMENICO, attributed to, Madonna and Child
    With St. John and St. Francis 30
BELLINI, GIOVANNI, Madonna and Child and St. John (?) 12
BELLINI, GIOVANNI, Madonna and Child 14
BOLOGNA, SIMONE DI FILIPPO DA, The Legend of St. Nicholas 4
BOSCH, HIERONYMUS, Ecce Homo 104
BOSCH, HIERONYMUS, School of, Temptation of St. Anthony 106
BOSSCHAERT, AMBROSIUS, The Younger, Flowers in a Glass Vase .. 86
BOTTICELLI, SANDRO, Circle of, Madonna and Child with
    St. John the Baptist 16
BOUT, PIETER and BOUDEWIJNS, ADRIAEN, Market Day 136
BRUEGHEL, JAN, The Elder, Canal Scene 118
BRUEGHEL, JAN, The Elder, Seascape with a High Cliff 120

CARAVAGGIO, MICHELANGELO MERISI DA, Sleeping Cupid 42
CASSATT, MARY, Mother and Child 168
CLAUDE GELLEE called CLAUDE LORRAIN, The Flight Into Egypt 154
CLOUET, FRANCOIS, Francois de Scepeaux 142
CLOUET, FRANCOIS, School of, King Charles IX of France (?) 144
CONSTABLE, JOHN, Harnham Bridge 96
CONSTABLE, JOHN, The Cornfield.. 98
CORNEILLE DE LYON, Marie de Guise 146
CORNEILLE DE LYON, Duchesse de Chatillon (?) 148
CORNEILLE DE LYON, Rene de Puy du Fou 150
CRANACH, LUCAS, The Elder, Crucifixion 176

DURER, ALBRECHT, attributed to, Dr. Christoph Scheurl, Jr. (?) 174

ENGLISH SCHOOL, ca. 1650, Portrait of a Lady 90

FOSCHI (or Toschi), PIER FRANCESCO DI JACOPO, St. Benizzi
    and the Gamblers 32
FOUQUET, JEAN, Jean Juvenal des Ursins II (?) 140
FRANCIA, FRANCESCO, Madonna and Child 22
FRENCH SCHOOL, 16th century, Abbess at Prayer 152
FRENCH SCHOOL, 19th century, Figures in a Landscape 166

GADDI, AGNOLO, Four Saints 6
GOVAERTS, ABRAHAM, Rest on the Flight into Egypt 130
GOYA Y LUCIENTES, FRANCISCO JOSE DE, attributed to,
    El Juego de Barras 70
GOYA Y LUCIENTES, FRANCISCO JOSE DE, attributed to,
    Portrait of a Little Girl 72
GOYA Y LUCIENTES, FRANCISCO JOSE DE, Holy Communion 74
EL GRECO, St. Matthew 50
EL GRECO, St. Simon 52
EL GRECO, St. Luke 54
EL GRECO, Christ Bearing the Cross 56
EL GRECO, School of, St. Judas Thaddaeus or St. Thomas (?) 58
GUARDI, FRANCESCO, Two Venetian Canal Scenes 44

HALS, FRANS, Self Portrait 78
HOLBEIN, HANS, The Younger, Self Portrait 178
HOLBEIN, HANS, The Younger, Portrait of an Unknown Lady 180
HOLBEIN, HANS, The Younger, attributed to, Thomas Cromwell 182

ISENBRANDT, ADRIAEN, Joseph and Mary in Bethlehem 110
ISENBRANDT, ADRIAEN, The Flight into Egypt 112
ISENBRANDT, ADRIAEN, follower of, Madonna and Child
    in a Landscape 114

LUINI, BERNARDINO, Madonna and Child with St. John and the
    Lamb 28

MAINARDI, SEBASTIANO, The Holy Family with St. John
    and an Angel 24
THE MASTER OF THE WINTER LANDSCAPES, attributed to,
    Winter Landscape 132
MURILLO, BARTOLOME ESTEBAN, Madonna in Prayer 68

NEROCCIO DEI LANDI, Madonna and Child with Sts. John and
    Mary Magdalene 20
SOUTH NETHERLANDISH MASTER, Holy Family with an Angel 116

PERUGINO, PIETRO DI CHRISTOFORO VANNUCCI, Christ on
    the Mount of Olives 18

REMBRANDT HARMENSZ. VAN RIJN, Self Portrait 82
REMBRANDT HARMENSZ. VAN RIJN, attributed to, Old Man
    with a Tall Fur-edged Cap 84
REYNOLDS, SIR JOSHUA, Mrs. Thomas Watkinson Payler 92
REYNOLDS, SIR JOSHUA, School of, Mrs. Charles James Fox 94
RIBERA, JUSEPE DE, Archimedes 60
ROBERT, HUBERT, La Statue 162
ROBERT, HUBERT, Italian Garden Scene 164

RUBENS, PETER PAUL, Triumphant Entry of Constantine into
    Rome 124
RUBENS, PETER PAUL, attributed to, Nobleman in Armor 126
RUBENS, PETER PAUL, School of, Man in a Ruff 128

LO SCARSELLINO (Ippolito Scarsella), Madonna and Child with
    St. John 38

TINTORETTO, JACOPO, attributed to, Apollo and the Muses 34
TITIAN (Tiziano Vecelli), attributed to, Andrea dei Franceschi 26

UCCELLO, PAOLO, attributed to, Profile of a Young Man 10

PERE VALL (The Master of the Cardona Pentecost), Two Pairs
    of Saints 48
VAN DEN BUNDEL, WILLEM, attributed to, A Lady with her
    Retinue beside a River 122
VAN DER WEYDEN, ROGIER, Portrait of a Man 102
VAN DYCK, SIR ANTHONY, attributed to, Self Portrait 134
VELAZQUEZ, DIEGO, attributed to, Still Life 64
VELAZQUEZ, DIEGO, School of, Portrait of a Lady 66

WATTEAU, JEAN ANTOINE, attributed to, Sheet of Studies 156
WATTEAU, JEAN ANTOINE, Circle of, Four Ladies 158
WATTEAU, JEAN ANTOINE, Circle of, Three Standing Ladies 160
WELLENS DE COCQ, JAN, Circle of, Landscape with Hermit 108
WILLAERTS, ABRAHAM, Seascape with Ruins on a Cliff 80

ZUCCHI, JACOPO, attributed to, Portrait of a Lady 36
ZURBARAN, FRANCISCO DE, School of, Stoning of a Dominican
    Martyr 62

OBJECTS IN THE CLOWES COLLECTION 187

SIT.
STAY.
SUCCEED!

Management
Lessons
from Man's
Best Friend

TREMENDOUS
LIFE BOOKS.com

Tremendous Life Books
118 West Allen Street
Mechanicsburg, PA 17055
www.TremendousLifeBooks.com
www.facebook.com/TremendousLifeBooks
www.twitter.com/TraceyCJones

Design and layout by Anthony R. Michalski

ISBN-13 978-1-936354-30-6

DESIGNED & PRINTED IN THE UNITED STATES OF AMERICA

The Table of Contents

Introduction i

Meet the Dogs iii

The KIMBA Principle 1

Choosing the Right Breed 11

Bringing the New Pup Home 21

Show Them the Way 29

Set Proper Boundaries 39

Determine Motivation 49

Respect the Old Dogs 61

Pavlov's Dog Talks to the Other Dogs 69

Prepare for the Occasional Accident 77

Don't Forget to Let Them Out to Play 87

About the Author 96

To the most important person in my life…
my wife Ann.
I love and appreciate all the support and contributions you
make in my projects.
Thank you for finding Baleigh and Kimba.
Also to my dad, who taught me the importance of
hard work,
dependability,
and making your own opportunities for success.

Introduction

Ifirst spoke about the principle in this book—the KIM-BA principle—at a luncheon for the Greater Bux-Mont Chamber of Commerce a couple of years ago. The members paid close attention as I detailed the five reasons for performance issues in the workplace.

Both during my talk and afterwards, I was besieged with questions and comments. The comments were overwhelmingly positive (thank you!) and the questions were from people who wanted, and maybe needed, more detail so that they could resolve an issue at their office.

Since then, I have spoken about the KIMBA principle in dozens of workshops and seminars to managers and employers of all shapes, sizes, nationalities, and businesses who were seeking solutions to employee issues.

A few times after I delivered my presentation, a person would ask, "So, why dogs? Are you implying that employees should be treated like dogs?"

My answer never failed to shock them. "Hopefully, yes!"

That may surprise you, too. Let me explain.

If the title, cover, and contents of this book haven't made it clear, I am a dog-lover. My two dogs, Kimba and Baleigh, who you'll meet in a page or two, are amongst the joys of my life. I meet many other owners of dogs who, more often than not, have one thing in common: they tend to treat their animals—their dogs—better than people! Consulting with businesses and corporations and meeting managers who, like myself, have a canine or two at home, I discovered that what they would do for their pet for training, care, and support often far outweighed what these very same people would do for the employees who worked with or under them.

Frankly, they treated their dogs a hundred times better than they'd even think to treat their employees!

And what has that got them? It got them "bones of contention" in the workplace, which lead to lowered productivity, workplace strife and discomfort, higher employee turnover rates, hampered growth, and many other debilitating results.

The solution is simple. As an employer, as a manager, as a supervisor, and even as a co-worker, you should endeavor to treat your employees like dogs! When you do that, then you'll see the results that you want to see—and that your business requires in order for it to grow.

In other words, take some lessons from man's best friend.

So, sit back.

Stay for a while.

And succeed with the principles I will share with you in this book.

Michael Patterson
April 2012

Meet the Dogs

Ann and I were only in our new house about six weeks when she asked a startling question: "Can we get a puppy?"

I was surprised, because my wife had never owned a dog before. She was a life-long cat owner. I, on the other hand, always had a dog.

Owning a dog is a lot of work. You can house-break a cat almost immediately by just pointing him to the litter box. A puppy, on the other hand, needs constant supervision and weeks and months of reinforcement to be house-broken. Also, while a cat is pretty self-sufficient, a dog needs interaction and playtime or he will chew up pretty much your entire house. A dog doesn't groom itself like a cat; it needs to be washed and brushed regularly.

Ann was sure she wanted a dog, so after a day or two we went to the local pet store on a warm summer night to look at puppies. Among the glass cases of canines, Ann spotted a black-and-white lab mix curled up in a ball all by herself. When we asked to see her, the dog immediately took to my wife and snuggled up in the crook of her neck. We knew we had a winner. We took her home and named her Baleigh.

A few months went by and, just after Thanksgiving, Ann decided Baleigh needed a companion. We went back to the same pet store and were attracted to a large litter of white German Shepherds. By this time Baleigh had been through puppy training and one of her class-mates was a white Shepherd, the first I had ever seen. We were looking for a male dog, and saw one off to the side playing with a red ball. We played with him a little, and later brought Baleigh back to play with him too. We now had the newest addition to our family.

Since winter was approaching, we toyed with cutesy names for a white dog, like Snowy and Blizzard, but we knew he was a stud in the making, so we decided on a stronger name and settled on Kimba.

That's how our two dogs came to be part of the family. But how did they come to teach us solid principles of coaching and mentoring?

Read on! It turns out that Kimba and Baleigh have a lot to share...

1

The KIMBA Principle

Your organization has goals, vision, values, and expectations for their employees. To be successful, your employees need to constantly meet and frequently exceed those expectations. Companies are challenged by their customers, shareholders, and business partners to always strive to be the best. The success of any organization, and of its management team, is entrusted in the hands of the average employee. It's true: they are the ones responsible for making or breaking the organization. It's the frontline employees who interact most with your customer base, uphold service standards, quell small issues from becoming major problems, and capitalize on opportunities to increase revenue. Small successes from dozens of employees each day ultimately lead to the overall well-being of the organization; it's the manager's job to help put it all together.

This is true of most any organization. In Major League Baseball, the manager gets credit for winning and blamed for losing, even though he never plays in a game. The best manager will never catch a ball, strike a batter out, or get a base hit. His responsibilities are to oversee the team, prepare his players for success, create a starting lineup, and make changes and substitutions as needed. It's his players' responsibility to perform the day-to-day tasks to make the team successful, just like it's your employees' responsibilities to do the same.

But what if employees sometimes come up a little short?

Baseball teams employ coaches to work with their players to maintain and improve performance. There are individual coaches to help players with specific duties such as hitting, pitching, fielding, and base running. The manager's job is to coordinate all of the individual coaches to achieve the team's overall goal of winning games. In other sports, the manager's title is head coach. Every player needs coaching. Whether you are the best hitter on the team or the worst, you practice with the hitting coach before each and every game. In the workplace, it is your responsibility to work with your best and worst employees for your team's success. You need to be able to coach and motivate your employees to maintain and improve performance.

As we appreciate and value each employee's individuality, we must recognize that not everyone comprehends, performs, and responds to goals the same way. Employees who do not perform as expected may be unfairly labeled as 'bad' employees. That's not necessarily the case. These employees may require additional guidance to enable them to perform to the best of their abilities. Managers who make a conscious effort to effectively coach and motivate their employees can bring out substantial improvement in performance.

Keep in mind that coaching and motivation are not the same as training. Training is required when an individual does not know how to perform a certain function, or when a new skill needs to be introduced. Coaching is developing or enhancing a set of skills the individual currently possesses to perform a function more successfully or effectively than they currently do. Motivation is providing an individual with an internal or external incentive to perform a task. All three are necessary tools to use to improve employee production.

While managers understand the need for coaching, training, and motivation to improve performance, many are not sure where to begin. During coaching workshops, managers come into the classroom drained of ideas on how to coach and motivate employees. One manager, Fred, was exasperated while explaining his dilemma. Fred told me he had no success coaching and motivating employees even though he had "tried everything." I could sense Fred's frustration, and really wanted to help. I asked him to take out a blank piece of paper and write down everything he tried. I could tell Fred was a busy guy, and there was no need to waste time rehashing all the unsuccessful ways he tried to motivate his employees in the past. I told him to write down everything he already tried so we could quickly discount those things and move forward.

The funny thing about asking Fred to write down everything he tried even though he said he "tried everything"—it was a pretty short list. When I say funny I mean in an ironic way, not a ha-ha way, because quite frankly, Fred wasn't laughing. While it is ironically funny, it is not surprising. Managers usually have a short list when it comes to ways to coach and motivate employees. When they say they have tried everything, what they are really saying is they tried everything they knew to try. Good thing for me; it keeps me in a job.

Many managers have been put into management positions because they worked their way through the ranks, excelling at previous jobs. I've known many managers with "Type-A" personalities. Sometimes dubbed workaholics, these are ambitious, aggressive, competitive individuals who multi-task and set goals. The drawback to "Type-A" personalities is impatience. Because of their nature, many managers found success through hard work, drive, and determination. They have a hard time comprehending why an employee needs to be motivated by a third-party to do a good job. They are self-motivated, and believe the personal thrill of a job well done and a goal achieved should be motivation enough.

Since they have trouble grasping the concept of third-party motivation, sometimes managers have trouble understanding why an employee does certain things one way, some things another, and other things not at all. Managers may feel they have a better understanding of their family pet at home than they do their employees at work. Maybe they would be better off taking their tips and cues from their dog!

If managers find it difficult to understand the needs, behaviors, and motivational factors of their employees, perhaps they should start with something more basic—understanding what drives the family dog. While I am certainly not comparing your employees to dogs, it's worth noting the cross-species similarities between certain needs, behaviors, and motivational factors.

- Both are loyal and want to please.
- Both may take their cues from certain pack leaders.
- Both may be motivated by rewards and appreciation.
- Both have different traits, skills, and characteristics which enable them to fill specific roles.
- Both need clear expectations and boundaries.

Throughout my career I have often been asked to get involved with "training issues" that weren't really training issues. Managers may cite the need for training when the issue is really more attributable to areas of coaching and motivation. To determine how to best handle poor performance, you need to uncover the root cause.

There are five factors that are the causes of poor performance. I named these factors after my dog and call it the **KIMBA principle**.

Knowledge

Does the employee know what to do, how to do

it, and why they are doing it? If an employee is responsible for sales, he or she must be acutely aware of how the product functions, and its features and benefits to the customer.

Inhibitors

Is there anything internal, external, tangible, or intangible preventing the employee from performing the task?

Motivation

Does the employee want to perform the job to the best of his or her ability? Are there rewards or repercussions based on how the employee performs?

Boundaries

Have you created guidelines which keep the employee on the right track to perform the job?

Abilities

Is the employee capable of performing the task?

You can use the KIMBA principle for any situation, whether you are coaching an employee at work, or training a new puppy at home. When we first got Baleigh, we wanted to train her to walk on a leash. When walking a dog, you want the dog to heel by your left side. There should be some slack in the leash. Obviously, Baleigh didn't know that. We couldn't communicate it to her verbally; we had to show her. So we started to train her to walk on a leash by providing her the knowledge. Motivation for Baleigh is pretty easy; she'll do anything for food and positive attention. We feed her twice a day, morning and night.

Instead of feeding her in her bowl at night, we took her food on the walk with us and every ten yards or so we gave her a small handful of dry kibble. That was all the motivation she needed to keep walking properly. Setting and keeping boundaries are always important when training dogs or employees. We wanted Baleigh to walk tight to our left side. If she started walking ahead, we stopped. If she walked over to the right side, we stopped and switched her to our left. Allowing her to walk wherever she wanted would reset the boundaries, which would have impeded the training.

Sometimes during our walks Baleigh is walking just the way we want her to when all of a sudden something happens. Maybe she sees another dog, a kid on a bicycle, a squirrel running across the street, or a car blaring a loud radio. These things get her attention and distract her from the task at hand. Those are the inhibitors. We can't always control inhibitors, and need to work to refocus Baleigh to ignore them and continue with her task at hand (or in her case, her task at paw).

Let's take a look at how the KIMBA principle also applies to your employees at work. The following scenario deals with an employee dress code issue:

You notice Christy has come to work today dressed inappropriately. You were told that last week, while you were on vacation, Christy was dressed the same way as today. Neither your assistant nor anyone else commented to Christy last week about the way she was dressed.

Let's take KIMBA out for a walk by determining

how to address the situation:

The first factor I always look at is knowledge. You may assume an employee knows what to do, but people don't know what they don't know, so knowledge is always a good place to start. Does your company have a written dress code? If so, was Christy made aware of it? Does the code include examples of unacceptable dress? If she usually dresses appropriately, perhaps Christy is aware of the code but doesn't realize this particular outfit is unacceptable. If this is a knowledge issue, all it will take is a brief discussion with Christy and your problem is solved.

Maybe Christy knows the dress code, but she just doesn't care to follow it. What she is wearing now is more comfortable, more stylish, or more expensive than the "acceptable wardrobe." Sure, she has seen the code, but supervisors really don't enforce it, do they? What's the worst that could happen? If this sounds familiar, then Christy's issue is with motivation. Dress code isn't a performance issue, and it's tough to reward someone for complying with non-performance issues. To motivate you need to explain what the repercussions are for not adhering to the dress code, and follow through if Christy does not comply in the future.

What if other employees dress the same way Christy did but nobody said or did anything about it? You were just informed Christy dressed the same way the week before and nothing was said to her. If there have been violations of the dress code by Christy or other employees without repercussions in the past, then the problem has to do with improperly setting boundaries. Remind employees of proper dress code, and address future issues of improper dress swiftly and forthrightly.

Inhibitors are often the last thing to look at just because there are so many variables to consider. The best way to approach this is to have an honest conversation with your employee. Maybe budget is a concern and Christy can only afford a limited number of outfits. Maybe she has a second job and is leaving for that right after work without time to change. Maybe she has a physical condition which makes it difficult to wear dress shoes. There are so many reasons, you really need to talk and find out. I once talked to a male employee about his dress. He used to dress neatly, wearing crisp dress shirts with matching tie and pants. Now his outfits were mismatched, and his shirts were badly in need of an iron. He explained to me he just split up with his girlfriend. They used to live together, and she coordinated and ironed all his clothes.

Throughout this book we will delve more deeply into understanding the five areas of KIMBA, and apply the same concepts we learned from our dogs to train, coach, and motivate employees. Obviously, employees are not pets. Under no circumstance should you strike employees with rolled-up newspapers or lock them in crates when you leave the office. Employees should be rewarded for good behavior, but I'm sure Human Resources would frown upon rubbing an employee's belly.

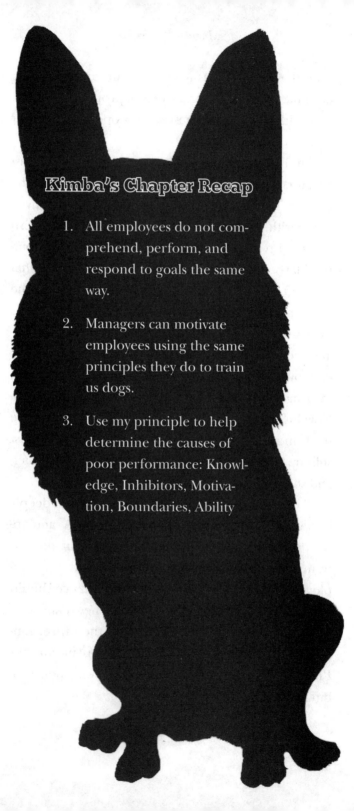

Kimba's Chapter Recap

1. All employees do not comprehend, perform, and respond to goals the same way.

2. Managers can motivate employees using the same principles they do to train us dogs.

3. Use my principle to help determine the causes of poor performance: Knowledge, Inhibitors, Motivation, Boundaries, Ability

2
Choosing the Right Breed

The American Kennel Club recognizes over 150 different breeds of dogs which are separated into eight breed groups depending on size, traits, function, and other characteristics.[*]

Choosing the right dog for your family is not as simple as picking out the cutest puppy behind the window. First, you need to know what role you want the dog to play in your home—you need to have a job description just like the job descriptions you create at work. Do you want the dog to be big, small, playful, or intimidating? Do you expect him to be a guard dog or lap dog?

When we chose our first dog, I kept in mind that my wife never had a dog before. A big, strong dog may have been too much to handle as a first dog. Neither of us wanted a small, yappy dog either. We wanted a medium-sized dog who would be both playful and affectionate. Baleigh is playful, and cuddles beside Ann every chance she gets. We were told Baleigh would get to be around 50 pounds, and that's what she is. Baleigh was the perfect fit for a first dog.

* *www.akc.org/breeds*

When we were looking for a companion for Baleigh, we had a different set of requirements. This time we wanted a larger, more protective dog. I wanted a male dog, as I was feeling a little overrun by females in the house. Of course, whatever we chose had to interact well with Baleigh. After doing a lot of research online, we narrowed our pool to just a few breeds. When we went to the pet store and found Kimba, we knew he was a great dog for us, but we were not the only ones he needed to impress. We knew we had to bring Baleigh to see how the two of them would interact. You could consider that to be Kimba's second interview!

Managers need to choose the right candidate for the job based on personality, qualifications, expectations, skill sets, and previous work experience. Each job at your organization requires different skills, so you are looking for different types of employees to fill those roles. Sometimes managers make the mistake of hiring or promoting the wrong employee for those positions. By not matching the right employee with the right role, managers are creating a skill gap from the beginning, which will require coaching and training more quickly than you may have anticipated.

The first step in the hiring process is to assess the need for your department. Assessing the need will help you determine the type of individual who would be the perfect fit for the vacant position. Evaluate the culture of your company; consider your vision, mission, and core values. Keep in mind it is much easier to train for skills than it is for values and attitudes.

You can always train a new employee to perform a task, but hiring an employee who doesn't possess the same values as you or your organization will be problematic in the long run. After aligning your values and attitudes, then focus on the individual's skills and abilities. Consider the following factors that will impact your success in finding the perfect fit.

Ensure there is an updated job description for the position.

A current and accurate job description will help you identify the skills, competencies, and characteristics necessary to fill the position. Competencies to look for include reading comprehension, math skills, computer skills, decision making, flexibility, and interpersonal skills. Consider which skills are essential, which tasks are performed occasionally, and which are not necessary for the job.

Determine the working conditions the position has to offer (work schedule, dress, expectations, accountabilities, sales requirements).

Don't ignore anything just because you think it might paint your organization in a negative light. In our credit union the branches are open seven days a week. Full-time branch employees are expected to work one or two weekends each month. This may be a deal-breaker for them, but at least we are all aware of the candidate's ability and willingness to work the schedule before we invest too much time on the interview process.

Determine how much experience and education is needed to fill the position and to address specific needs.

Some jobs can allow for a training period, while others require the employee to 'hit the ground running' almost from day one. Understand that even the employee with the best credentials will need a period of time to get adjusted to your organization's specific culture.

Determine the appropriate compensation for the position.

In larger companies, this is usually handled by the payroll or human resources department. Many companies have a salary structure which includes a minimum and maximum pay for each position. Employees with no prior experience are usually brought in at the minimum, and those with experience are brought in at a higher pay. Also keep in mind you are looking to pay for the job the employee is performing and not necessarily the skills or expertise the employee possesses. If an individual with 15 years of banking experience who has been a branch manager applies for a teller position, that person is going to be paid within the scale of a teller, not a manager.

Choosing the wrong individual for a job can lead to the same frustrating, disastrous results as choosing the wrong dog for a family. After seeing the live-action *101 Dalmatians*, my friends Frank and Allison brought home a new Dalmatian puppy. They loved the dog and agreed to name him Elvis after one of

Frank's favorite singers. Unfortunately, Frank and Allison didn't do their proper homework on the breed. They didn't realize that, while cute, these dogs tend to be extremely hyper as puppies and need a lot of play and interaction. The family wasn't able to be as attentive to Elvis as he needed them to be. As a result, Elvis chewed everything. He started with shoes, and graduated to a chair, a sofa, and eventually the drywall! Elvis wasn't necessarily a bad dog. This was more a case of a bad match between dog and family that led to bad results.

In the business world, a bad match between employee and job duties can create bad results as well. In banking, a teller is an entry-level position. To be a good teller, the employee needs to be good at cash handling and interacting with customers. He or she needs to develop speed to perform transactions quickly, while still maintaining accuracy. We sometimes hire new tellers with prior banking experience, and other times we hire them with prior customer service or cash handling experience in another field. When we hire new tellers without any type of prior experience, we look for individuals who have friendly personalities. Tellers are the front-line employee; customers see them more than they do any other employee in the bank. If a teller has a negative personality or is not engaging, it may create a negative experience for the customer. Since our profession is all about service and trust, a few negative experiences may cause customers to take their money elsewhere.

Your profession also has front-line employees.

Perhaps your company has receptionists, cashiers, salespeople, or telephone operators. These are the individuals who are the first point of contact for your customers, and with whom your customers interact the most. If you fill these positions with people who do not have a positive personality and a service-first mentality, you could impact customer relations. Competition for the consumer dollar is fierce. People are willing to pay more for better service. Bad customer relations will affect your company's bottom line.

Duties, responsibilities, and expectations often change. Our dogs love to run around and chase each other outside. Summer temperatures in our area can approach 100 degrees. When it gets this hot, we limit how much time our dogs spend outside. Just because we limit their time outside doesn't mean their desire to play is limited too. Of course, they can't run around in the house the same way they do outside without crashing into tables and breaking something. Our dogs need extra monitoring and different boundaries to play inside. Of course, accidents will still happen, but we need to limit the frequency and severity of those accidents. We changed their routine, environment, and expectations, and we need to make sure our dogs can adapt.

We've already distinguished a teller as an entry-level position. The next level up from a teller is a customer sales/service representative. This employee is responsible for opening new accounts, solving customer problems, taking loan applications, and discussing and selling additional products. The average transaction with this employee could last ten minutes or more compared to an average teller transaction of less than a minute.

Sometimes the employee who once excelled as a teller now struggles in his or her new position. This is the same, hard-working, devoted employee as before. Nothing has changed regarding attitude, determination, or intelligence. It's the job requirements that have changed. The fact is the skill sets required to be an effective and successful teller are not the same skills needed for the new job. When managers promote based on past successes, and neglect to consider the new job requirements, they inadvertently may set the employee up for failure.

The one area of the KIMBA principle we didn't discuss in the opening chapter is *ability*. When selecting someone for a position, managers need to measure if the individual has the ability to perform the job.

Many abilities can be trained; it depends on how much time and resources the organization is willing to spend to get new hires up to speed. Employees are expected to possess certain basic skills and most businesses understand that new hires may need trained on a specific computer system, but they shouldn't have to show someone how to use a mouse and keyboard.

During the hiring process, many organizations utilize tools such as pre-screening tests and assessments to measure a candidate's ability to perform the job. At our organization, we use an online teller test to measure candidates' abilities in math, member service skills, and following directions. We use another test to gauge their attitudes toward attendance, punctuality, and quality of work. These assessments allow us to look at the candidates' abilities in ways that wouldn't be uncovered during a routine job interview.

John Caspole is president of Assessment Specialists, a company that administers employee assessment tests on behalf of Profiles International. Caspole believes that an assessment is vital to an organization's hiring practices because "gut-feel hiring works far less than 50% of the time. Getting an unbiased scientific measure of the candidate and how they fit the job helps employers avoid costly hiring mistakes. Interviewing candidates can be like seeing an iceberg in the ocean. You only see what is on the surface. Good job-fit tools allow you to see what is hidden during the interview but will assure or impede success on the job! Hiring the right person at the right time is a competitive advantage saving companies thousands of dollars while adding to the top line, especially within key business development situations."

Putting someone in the right job is the first step to creating a productive employee. Some people were made to be accountants, some to be salespeople, and others to work with their hands. Putting people in a position which is not the right fit for their skills, abilities, and personalities is sure to create coaching needs in the future.

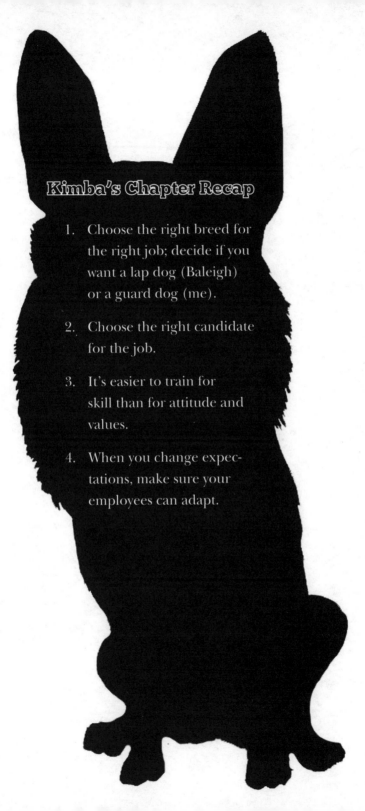

Kimba's Chapter Recap

1. Choose the right breed for the right job; decide if you want a lap dog (Baleigh) or a guard dog (me).

2. Choose the right candidate for the job.

3. It's easier to train for skill than for attitude and values.

4. When you change expectations, make sure your employees can adapt.

3
Bringing the New Pup Home

For a dog owner, nothing beats the day you bring your new puppy into your home for the very first time. It doesn't matter if you purchased the puppy from a pet store, individual breeder, or rescued him from a shelter; he is now coming home with you. The first day home the puppy wants to investigate his new environment. He will walk from room to room checking out the sights and sniffing the scents. He is curious from day one, and you need to monitor where he's going and what he's doing. You follow him around because you know there is a lot of trouble he can get into if left unattended on his own.

I often remind Ann that when you have two dogs and you can't see or hear what they are doing, it's probably not a good thing! A puppy may know how to get into things he can't get out of, like behind a table or on the bed. When teething, a puppy will chew just about anything. His plastic bone is not nearly as appetizing as your new pair of Nikes. Your puppy is also developing bladder control. He may know to go outside, and may meet you at the back door, but he isn't waiting around for long. If you don't properly monitor behavior, you will have an unexpected mess to clean up.

New employees in your office will want to investigate their new environment as well. From entry-level positions on up, new employees need a structured training and indoctrination process to understand policies, procedures, and company culture. A structured new-hire orientation program starting on day one, or before, will help lay out the environment for the employee. In addition to completing all of the necessary paperwork and learning company policies, employees should meet their new co-workers, discover the break and restrooms, and learn about any groups or activities in the organization. Understand that the employee will have questions as the days, weeks, and months go on, so make sure he or she has an outlet to obtain the correct answers in a timely manner after orientation.

Managers should monitor employees' behavior from the very first day, and continue to do so throughout their careers with your organization. Monitoring behavior is not the same thing as micromanaging, spying on, or smothering your employee. Monitoring behavior allows you to see what your employees are doing, and how they are doing it, which are both crucial to the coaching process. If an employee is not meeting expectations, but you don't know what, specifically, they are doing, then you won't know how to work with him or her to improve performance.

You cannot coach an employee to obtain a goal. Achieving goals is a result of doing individual tasks

well. A coach once told me that winning a champi-
onship is not a goal; it's the byproduct of hard work.
When training managers to coach employees and
provide feedback, I instruct them to focus on specific
employee behaviors. The behaviors are the individual
tasks which lead to achieving goals. By my definition,
a behavior is something which is:

- observable
- measurable
- specific
- based on fact

Let's look at each of the four parts, one by one, to
see how important each of them is to properly offer
feedback to coach your employee.

Observable

You have to be the one to actually see an action
occur, or expected action not occur. Remember the
time you spent housebreaking your new puppy? Now
imagine walking into the kitchen only to find your
cute, adorable dog has just left you a present on
the tile floor. Obviously, you didn't need to observe
the act to know what happened, but you did need
to observe it to know why it happened. The kitchen
leads to your back door, so the dog was halfway there.
Maybe he tried to get your attention but you didn't
notice. When we were housebreaking our dogs, they
would know to go to the back door when they needed to go out. They hadn't learned at the time to get
us; maybe they didn't have the control to wait. If we
would have monitored their behavior, we would have
noticed they were trying to do the right thing and no-

tify us they needed to go out. By observing behaviors, now we know any time the dogs go to the back door they need to go out.

Managers must put themselves in a position to interact with and observe the actions of their employees. Managers who manage from behind their office door are not effective coaches. While you can rely on information from others, to effectively coach your employees you need to witness the behavior with your own eyes. Maybe there is something you notice the employee doing that others would not. In professional baseball, the hitting coach spends hours watching video of his players batting. He is looking for subtleties in their stance, footwork, and hand position to help improve their swing. Improved swings lead to better opportunities to get hits. By observing an employee with low sales numbers, you can see his sales technique first-hand. You can tell if he knows his product, knows the benefits it offers the customer, and how confident he is in his delivery. Maybe the customer is giving off a sign which is obvious to you based on years of experience but would go unnoticed to your employee. If you are not there to notice the actions, all you can rely on are the final sales numbers, and not the causes for the lack of sales.

A few years into my career as a bank trainer, I was working out of an office in Philadelphia. My boss, Gary, worked out of Long Island. The distance between our offices was 300 miles, and Gary rarely came down to observe my classes. When it came time to provide me with feedback, the most he had to go on were the evaluations completed by participants after class. If I would get a low score or negative comment on an evaluation, how should Gary address that? Maybe my message wasn't clear to that employee, I didn't answer his/her questions, or maybe I was just plain rude! On the other hand, maybe the participant didn't want to be in the class or was resistant to learning something new. Gary couldn't coach me to deliver a better presentation for that employee when he didn't know what the problem was in the first place.

Observing behaviors makes the coaching process easier for the manager, and provides feedback which is direct and clear.

Measurable

Employees' actions, or the result of their actions, must be measured by either time, cost, growth, loss, or volume.

When we first took Baleigh to puppy training, one of her first lessons was to sit and stay. The trainer had us practice with Baleigh each day and time how long she would stay before she moved. When we started, we were lucky to get her to stay for more than two or three seconds. Every day after work we practiced with her and timed how long she would stay. As the days went by, she stayed longer and longer. By timing the activity, we had clear-cut measurable data to show her behavior was improving.

Your employee's actions result in performance which can be directly measured against expectations, past performance, and peer performance. A completed project can be measured by accuracy, timeliness, and cost. Sales results can be measured in volume, and compared to peer results or prior-year totals.

Specific

You need to be able to reference exactly what happened, and where and when it occurred. Avoid using generalities like 'always' and 'never'. No matter how much of a high or low performer your employee is, it is almost certain your employee doesn't 'always' or 'never' do something regarding work performance.

When coaching an employee with an attendance issue, avoid general statements like "frequently late." Instead, replace it with the more specific "Over 10 minutes late 5 times in the past month." Even better, list the actual dates and times. A "sloppy report" should reference specific instances of misspellings and poor grammar. By referencing specific behaviors, the employee knows exactly what the action was in comparison to the expectations. Employees will be less likely to argue or question feedback when you provide specific examples.

Always provide feedback in a timely manner; if not immediately following the incident, then within a day or two. By not providing timely feedback, the employee may believe his or her behavior is acceptable, and is likely to repeat it again. Delayed feedback may also result in the manager inadvertently setting new boundaries.

Based on Fact

If your feedback followed the first three steps, you should have no worries about complying with this one. When presented with indisputable facts, your employee will know what he or she did wrong, and what is needed to improve. If you've ever caught your dog in the act of chewing your brand-new shoes, you know the dog will usually cower away and hide. He knows you have an indisputable fact, and there's nothing he can do to deny it.

One final point about monitoring behavior: don't ignore your top performers. Managers will often overlook the top performers because they rationalize "if it ain't broke, don't try and fix it" or "no news is good news." Top performers want to be engaged, and might fall into a rut if they believe they are being underappreciated or if their work is becoming dull or predictable. Some employees crave attention from the boss, and might be put off because the new or struggling employee is getting all of the boss's time. When we brought Kimba home he needed more supervision than Baleigh, but Baleigh still wanted our attention too. A dog who was not previously a chewer might start chewing on the furniture if he knows it will get him some attention.

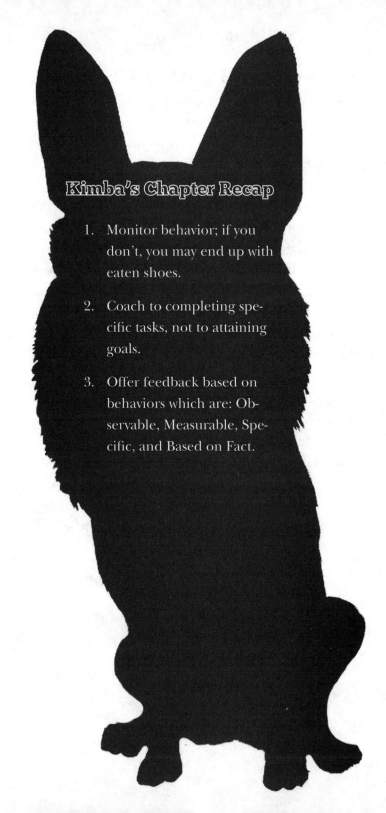

Kimba's Chapter Recap

1. Monitor behavior; if you don't, you may end up with eaten shoes.

2. Coach to completing specific tasks, not to attaining goals.

3. Offer feedback based on behaviors which are: Observable, Measurable, Specific, and Based on Fact.

4
Show Them the Way

Of all the dogs I've ever owned, Kimba has to be the "coolest" one. We did some online research about the temperament of white German Shepherds before we got him. All the sites touted the breed as loyal, protective, and loving. Some of the sites referred to it as being somewhat aloof and curious. Kimba definitely possesses the last two characteristics. He was stubborn to train, and "no" was a common command.

Dogs don't know what they are supposed to do unless we take the time to show them. Early commands for a new puppy focus on stopping negative behaviors. "No," "off," and "leave it" all tell a puppy what not to do; but just as much time should be spent encouraging an alternate, positive behavior. Instead of solely reprimanding your dog for chewing on your shoe, offer him a bone or toy, something you want him to chew on instead. By providing some direction, you are showing him your expectations of positive behavior. The dog will likely comply. After all, most dogs crave attention, affection, and treats!

Your employees also need direction. Managers assume employees know what is expected of them, but often that is not the case. Coaching workshops deal a lot with discovering and understanding what we refer to as the gap, the difference between how the employee is performing compared to expectations. Refer back to the first area of the KIMBA principle: *knowledge.* Does the employee have the necessary knowledge to do the job the way you expect it to be done? When considering knowledge, answer the following questions as they relate to the employee and task/role/responsibly assigned:

The employee must know:

- specifically what he/she is expected to do,
- how to do it,
- when it needs to be done,
- why it needs to be done,
- the benefits of doing it as expected,
- the repercussions for not doing it as expected.

It makes sense to inform employees what you expect them to do and to show them how to do it. It's so easy to do it that it's often not done! Managers need to provide their employees with the proper knowledge, and provide it in such a way that it's engaging to the employee. Merely telling an employee what to do isn't always enough. There is an old Native American saying which is often used in training.

Tell me and I will forget. Show me and I may remember. Involve me and I will understand.

A dog cannot understand things you tell him to

do. (Managers may argue the same can be said about certain employees.) A dog doesn't speak the same language as we do. To train a dog, you must involve him in the activity you want him to accomplish.

We crate our dogs when we are not home. Dogs are comfortable in their crate, but they don't know to go in it by themselves at first. If we told Baleigh and Kimba to go into the crate, they wouldn't know what that meant. We had to show them. We put treats and their toys in the crate to entice them in. We also used the word "crate" when they went in successfully. Before long, we could call out "Baleigh crate, Kimba crate" and they would run down the steps into their crates. Today, the dogs know our routine. As we are gathering up our stuff to go out, both will go into their crates without us having to say anything at all! Show dogs what to do and they will develop a routine to do it. Employees need to be shown what to do as well.

I recently conducted a workshop in which a manager shared her frustration with the lack of initiative on display from two of her new employees. During slow periods, they would just stand around and talk or surf the Internet. She expected them to be more self-motivated and to take the initiative to be more productive with their time. I agreed with her about how frustrating this situation can be, and asked what she expected from them when things were slow. Her response wasn't specific; it was only that the employees should "find something productive to do." That's the root of the problem right there. If the manager doesn't specifically know what the employees should do, the employees can't be expected to know either. Employees "don't know what they don't know." If expectations were never communicated to them, they can't be held accountable for not following through.

Have you ever stopped to think about how much time you spend telling a low-performing employee what not to do as opposed to what you expect them to do? This leaves employees guessing, and creates a frustrating situation for both you and your employee. I believe most employees want to do the right thing at work, but may not know what that is or how to do it. In a busy, fast-paced environment, sometimes the simple task of clearly communicating expectations gets forgotten. This is especially true if your department is predominately seasoned veterans.

If you are not sure if the employee understands your expectations, ask him or her to explain them back to you in their own words. As managers, we expect our employees to speak up and ask questions, but they may be afraid to do so, especially if they have a new relationship with their boss. Is it really their fault if they don't ask and get it wrong?

Organizations should have a structured onboarding process for new employees, which allows expectations to be set and communicated from day one. A friend of mine recently began a new job at a large company. Her onboarding process basically consisted of being issued a laptop and told she would pick things up as she went along. Not only did this create an environment for underperformance, it was unbelievably stressful. My friend wanted to perform well, but wasn't given the proper training or instructions to do so.

Without the proper training, mistakes are going to happen. In a stressful environment, employees' mistakes are going to be more common. Here is where the ugly snowball effect takes place. Stress leads to more mistakes which lead to more stress which leads to more mistakes. We are now faced with a disciplinary situation that could have possibly been avoided if the manager set clear expectations from the beginning.

Sandra Anderson, Human Resources Director for 1st Community Credit Union in Sparta, Wisconsin, stresses the importance of setting clear expectations. Anderson has found "until you inspect what the employee is doing and hold them accountable to the expectation, the manager, employee, and credit union will not be successful." 1st Community creates clear, concise expectations by using the PRICE method.

Pinpoint

Determine the performance area of interest.

Record

Measure current performance levels.

Involve

Gain the employee's buy-in by agreeing on performance goals and strategies for coaching and evaluating.

Coach

Observe performance and provide specific feedback.

Evaluate

Track performance and measure changes.

Another area that requires setting clear expectations is delegation. As a manager, I am sure you have delegated assignments to your staff from time to time. It's is a great tool for managers to begin developing employees for advancement by providing an opportunity to tackle additional responsibilities. John C. Maxwell, author of numerous leadership books including *The 21 Irrefutable Laws of Leadership*, once polled hundreds of CEOs and discovered that delegation was one of the most frequently mentioned important traits of a highly effective leader. Effective delegation is often underused by managers. Some argue it's just as easy to complete a task themselves than it is to give it to an employee, or the employee isn't able to complete the task as well as they can. This may be true; delegated assignments may not be completed as expected. Perhaps this could have something to do with managers not setting clear expectations. Consider the following scenario, and decide if it may sound familiar to you.

It is ten o'clock in the morning and the department manager, Kate, has a report which she needs completed by the end of the day for a meeting first thing the following morning. Kate takes the information needed to complete the report and walks over to the desk of one of her employees, Gene. "Hi Gene," Kate says, "I need you to complete the sales report for me. You did it for me last month, it's pretty simple. No rush; whenever you get around to it." Kate added the last line because she thought it sounded nicer than saying "by the end of the day." She knew it would only take Gene 20 or 30 minutes to complete, and besides, he didn't appear to be too busy. As the day progressed, Kate never went back to check up with Gene. Now it is 4:30 in the afternoon and Kate comes around to Gene's desk looking for the report. When she asks Gene if it is completed, he responds "Not yet, I haven't gotten around to it." Kate leaves Gene's desk upset and disappointed in his lack of productivity and motivation, and questions whether she will give him more assignments in the future. Now Kate is feeling stressed as she needs to stay late and complete this report herself before tomorrow's meeting.

Maybe you had a situation similar to the one above happen to you or another manager you know. It's another example of not setting clear expectations. I agree that Gene shares some blame for not verifying when Kate needed the report completed. Kate could have avoided the miscommunication in the first place by setting clear expectations up front. Now, not only is she forced to complete the report herself at the last minute, but she also may have damaged a relationship with an employee she might have been developing for a future promotion.

When training employees, as much as you need to tell them "what" they need to do and "how" they need to do it, it is equally important that they understand "why" they need to do it in a specific way. When an employee comprehends why a task needs to be completed and done in a specific way, you get the employee's buy-in. With their buy-in, the employee is more likely to complete the task appropriately. Understanding why a task needs to be done in a certain way, along with the repercussions for not following directions, will help your employee avoid implementing his or her own shortcuts. As we know, shortcuts sometimes work, and other times they cause problems. By nature, many of us tend to look for a quicker or easier way to do something. Unfortunately, those quicker ways may come at a cost.

Implementing shortcuts without understanding the 'whys' can cause problems both inside and outside of work. Let's say you were going to cook a chicken dinner tonight after work. You get out the chicken and look at the first two directions for preparing the meal:

1. Pre-heat oven to 350° F.
2. Bake for 30 minutes.

What if you were rushed for time and wanted to take a shortcut and didn't pre-heat the oven? If you don't understand why it's important then you might not know the oven takes five minutes to warm up to 350° F. By not allowing it to preheat, you are not cooking the chicken at the required temperature the entire time. The chicken won't cook thoroughly, which could sicken whomever eats it. This is definitely an example of a shortcut which can cause negative consequences.

Consider potentially dangerous shortcuts in your company. Tellers and cashiers are trained to count money twice or even three times before paying it to the customer. Contractors are trained to measure twice before cutting. Thinking one time was enough might leave them missing money from their cash drawer or with a piece of wood too short to use. Employees who understand why they do something a certain way, and the negative consequences for not following directions, will be more likely to complete a task the way it was intended. When this happens, everyone is happy.

Instructions to employees should be specific, clear, and to the point. The more confusing and vague the instructions, the more likely the employee won't know what is expected. If they don't know what to do, then they won't do what you want. You want to provide details, just make sure you don't overwhelm them with minutia. A five-page procedure on how to do something that could be explained in a one-page document isn't necessarily being thorough—it's overkill. The sheer size of the procedure may confuse employees. In the Gettysburg Address, Abraham Lincoln set the stage for preserving democracy and reuniting the country, and he needed less than 300 words to do it.[*]

---

[*] *www.ourdocuments.gov*

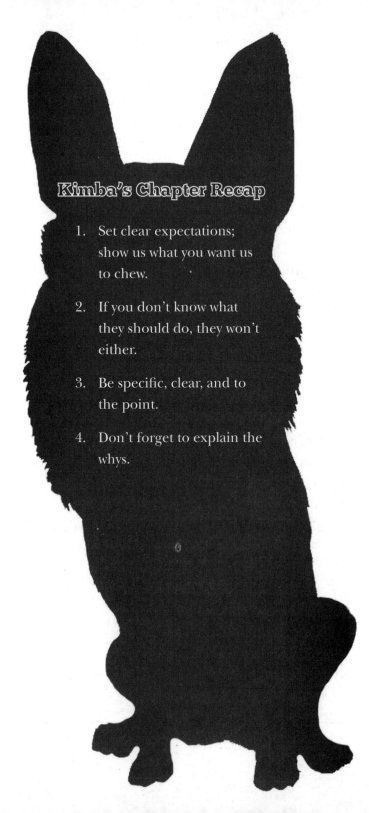

Kimba's Chapter Recap

1. Set clear expectations; show us what you want us to chew.

2. If you don't know what they should do, they won't either.

3. Be specific, clear, and to the point.

4. Don't forget to explain the whys.

5
Set Proper Boundaries

My wife and I both enjoy decorating the house for Christmas. We put the tree in the formal living room because it's the biggest room and it also allows us to put up a couple of baby gates to block the dogs from getting in. Our dogs like to play, and sometimes they play pretty rough. They bite each other to start a chase which is pretty funny to watch when they are outside during the spring, summer, and fall. Once December comes, they aren't outside too much, and their running around is limited to inside the house. If we didn't gate off the living room, our Christmas tree wouldn't stand a chance. Honestly, it just wouldn't stand at all!

We know we have to set proper boundaries to protect our house from the dogs, and also to protect our dogs from things in the house. We replaced the open trash can in the bathroom with a taller one with a lid to keep the dogs from the trash. We wouldn't want them to pull something out of the trash that may harm them. Our dogs love to eat old dryer sheets. While it may help their breath, I'm sure it's not good for them, so we make sure we discard the sheets out of the dogs' reach.

Everywhere you go there are boundaries. Cigarette smoking is legal, but more and more businesses are creating smoke-free areas. When I first flew on an airplane, there were rows designated as smoking rows. Now, smokers can't smoke anywhere in the airport, and can't even carry a lighter through the security checkpoints. Cell-phone talking is banned in movie theaters and most doctor's offices. Some upscale restaurants and night clubs still require patrons to comply with specific dress codes to be served. These policies are created to enhance the experience of those around you.

In your organization, boundaries are created in the form of policies, procedures, standards, and core values. They are designed for the safety and benefit of the individual employee, co-worker, customers, and organization as a whole. Boundaries can be set by the organization itself, such as limitations for merchandise returns at a store. Boundaries can also be set by federal regulations such as HIPAA requirements which limit what information medical personnel can discuss about a patient. Your business might supply new employees with an employee handbook during their first day of orientation, providing them with set boundaries.

Setting proper boundaries is different from setting clear expectations as discussed in the previous chapter. Expectations are the tasks you want employees to accomplish, and boundaries are the guidelines you want them to follow while they are accomplishing those tasks. Boundaries are designed to keep the employee on the right track while reaching the company's goals. Think of them as the yellow line, guard rail, and speed limit for the highway. Let's say you work in sales and the expectations are to sell 'x' number of products to customers by the end of the month. One boundary would be that the sales are ethical; you don't sell a product to someone who cannot afford it, has no real need for it, and will never use it. Another boundary would be that the sale has to be profitable to the organization.

In large commercial banks, tellers are expected to refer checking accounts to customers. This is one way the banks monitor growth, by increasing what they call their core deposits: checking and savings accounts. So each teller might be required to refer ten new checking accounts each month. These are the expectations. The organization wants these accounts to be profitable, so they need to be legitimate referrals to customers who are going to maintain a balance and use the account. These are the boundaries. I've witnessed managers who stress the goal of new accounts so much that they stretch the boundaries. A teller may refer a checking account to a customer who already has three accounts, so it's opened with only $1 and never touched again. This is not a profitable account, yet the employee is being rewarded for referring it. In the long run, the goal may be met, but the organization actually loses money.

Different boundaries can also be set based upon an employee's position and experience. In lending, underwriters have different loan-approval limits depending upon their position. In medicine, within the Commonwealth of Pennsylvania, nurse practitioners can write prescriptions for most drugs, but not for narcotics. These boundaries were created because it was decided that more schooling and experience were needed for the added responsibilities that come with prescribing narcotics.

Different boundaries may be instituted in your organization, too. An employee who is new to your company may not be afforded the same authority and autonomy as someone who has been there for years. In our credit union, tellers have different limits depending on their experience. The larger the dollar amount, the bigger potential loss if the transaction is performed incorrectly. Once a teller reaches their limit, the transaction must be reviewed and approved by a supervisor.

The use of a probationary period for new hires is another example of a boundary instituted at work. In many organizations, newly hired employees work in a probationary period of 60 or 90 days. During this time there may be restrictions on health benefits and paid days off. Their performance may be watched more closely to determine if they really do possess the skills necessary to complete their duties and responsibilities. New employees may be teamed up with a seasoned employee to observe and learn the on-the-job duties in a process called "shadowing." After a couple weeks the shadowing may reverse, and the seasoned employee is observing the new employee to evaluate and report back to the supervisor. Companies may find it easier to terminate employment during the probationary period than at any other time.

While guidelines are often created to prevent employees from making costly mistakes, there are times the boundaries create roadblocks which impede employees from performing their job duties effectively. Earlier I mentioned a new teller with a dollar limit on transactions. While this policy helps protect the bank against loss due to fraud, it could create losses elsewhere. Since newer tellers must get more checks approved by their supervisors, there is an increase to the wait time for the customer who is being waited on, and for the other customers in line. These customers may grow impatient and unhappy, and unhappy customers tend to take their business elsewhere. It also takes the supervisor away from whatever he or she was previously doing. Placing boundaries can create both risks and rewards. In this scenario, the reward was reducing fraud, the risk was customer impact. To create a policy that works, organizations must decide how much fraud they are willing to risk to maintain customer satisfaction. A happy customer probably doesn't offset a $10,000 loss, but it is not worth upsetting a customer to review a $50 check.

Economic frugality can create boundaries that impede employee production, too. Reducing staff puts a larger burden on the remaining employees. Eight employees may not be able to produce what ten did before, and decreased morale may lead to lack of production as well. Companies may try and save money on supplies, equipment upgrades and maintenance, and other resources which are necessary for employees to perform their jobs effectively. Roof-Roof Dog Toys, an online company, decided to save the money earmarked for computer and software upgrades. By using slow and outdated equipment, employees could not process as efficiently as their counterparts working for the competition. Employees became frustrated, and some even left Roof-Roof to work for the competition. Production decreased, as did revenue. Ultimately, Roof-Roof decided the new computers were necessary after all. In the meantime, the boundaries of not supplying proper equipment had a negative effect on their bottom line.

Through their actions, and sometimes inactions, managers may inadvertently set new boundaries they didn't mean to create. The biggest pet peeve (pun intended) I had about our dogs is how excited they got when friends and family came over to our house. Kimba would jump on guests, and he is a large dog. Our dog trainer instructed us to have guests turn their backs to him when he jumped. Kimba only wanted attention, but jumping up on guests is a boundary. When guests engaged him by petting him rather than turning their backs, they were giving him the attention he wanted and rewarding negative behavior. They were also reestablishing the boundaries.

In the opening chapter we talked about Christy, the employee with the dress code issue. By not discussing her inappropriate dress the week before, and by allowing other employees to dress the same way, her manager was resetting the dress code boundary. While the policy wasn't officially changed, what was considered to be acceptable behavior did change. Allowing employees to conduct themselves in a particular way creates workplace precedence and resets boundaries. Not only can this affect one manager's employees, it can also affect employees in other departments. If the manager of Christy's co-worker lets that person dress in a certain way, Christy will believe it won't be a problem for her to dress the same way too.

Since you have mistakenly moved the boundary, you now need to move it back. Managers can use this 4R method to communicate unacceptable behavior, reiterate expectations, and accept blame for moving the boundary. The four Rs in the 4R method stand for **R**equirement, **R**equest, **R**espect, and **R**esult.

Here is an example of how the manager can utilize the 4R method when addressing Christy about her dress code issue:

(*Requirement*) Christy, the company has a specific dress code policy which does not allow sleeveless shirts. (*Request*) I need you to adhere to the policy and stop wearing shirts such as the one you are wearing. (*Respect*) I understand we have not addressed this in the past when you and your co-workers dressed inappropriately. (*Result*) However, going forward, we will be holding all employees accountable for adhering to dress code standards.

In the scenario above, the manager took responsibility for moving the boundary with the respect statement: "I understand we have not addressed this in the past when you and co-workers dressed inappropriately." This is an important admission for the manager to make. Your employee knows the boundaries weren't in place before, and she needs to know why they are being put into place now.

Remember, setting boundaries is not a bad thing. In a previous chapter I discussed how we crate our dogs when we're not home. Being placed in a crate is the ultimate boundary. (For the record, human resources departments throughout the country will frown on using the crate method for employees!) We don't crate them because we don't love them; quite the opposite. We crate them to keep them out of trouble and to prevent them from hurting themselves. It would be horrible if they ran around the house and knocked a lamp or a table over on top of themselves. It would be even worse if one of them started chewing on a cord plugged into an electrical outlet.

Your employees also expect to receive guidelines on what to do, or not, and what's acceptable behavior, or not. Setting proper boundaries is really about doing what's right for your employees and the organization. Remember, sometimes you have to put them on a short leash!

Kimba's Chapter Recap

1. Set proper boundaries.

2. Boundaries protect the employee and the organization.

3. Be careful to not recreate boundaries.

4. Sometimes you have to use a short leash.

6
Determine Motivation

As much as you may consider your dog to be an extension of your family, he doesn't speak or understand English. He doesn't understand Spanish, French, German, or any other language either. A dog doesn't understand what you mean when you ask him to sit, stay, lay down, or any other command you give him. Dogs learn these commands because you show them what to do, and because there is something in it for them when they comply. You reward them with treats, toys, or affection. Maybe the time spent playing is reward enough. Some breeds want to please their owner by nature, so they are easy to train. Many are food motivated and will follow commands for a treat.

Baleigh was an easy dog to train, because she was motivated by both food and affection. Kimba isn't as food-motivated as Baleigh. Don't get me wrong, that boy eats; he just isn't as likely to sit for an extended period of time for a Milk-Bone. Kimba is more active, and likes to play with his toys, look out the window at who is walking down the street, and such. He likes to play fetch, so we need to involve him in activities to keep his interest and keep him motivated. Not all dogs like to play with or eat the same things. Walk into a local PETCO or PetSmart and you will see dozens of flavors of dog food and treats, and hundreds of different types of dog toys. We have a container of toys in our living room. There are some toys Kimba loves to play with that Baleigh won't touch. Then there are others they fight over. Just because one cherishes a reward doesn't mean they both will.

Employees are motivated by different things. They cherish their different toys as well. Some employees are motivated by money, the chance of promotion, a day off, free lunch, or personal recognition from their supervisor. What motivates one employee may not motivate another, and what motivates you may not motivate them. Discover what motivates each of your employees by talking with and getting to know them. Understand what your employees care about most, and use it to create a reward structure catered specifically to them.

People are motivated by their reasons—not yours

Steven Reiss, a professor of psychology and psychiatry at Ohio State University, devoted 5 years studying more than 6,000 individuals to determine what motivates people. His findings were published in his book *Who Am I? The 16 Basic Desires That Motivate Our Actions and Define Our Personalities.*[*] He discovered that individuals' behavior was motivated by 16 basic desires.

---

[*] Tarcher/Putnam, 2000.

Power	*Social Contact*
Independence	*Family*
Curiosity	*Status*
Acceptance	*Vengeance*
Order	*Romance*
Saving	*Eating*
Honor	*Physical Exercise*
Idealism	*Tranquility*

Understanding that people are motivated by their reasons and not yours is the most important concept to remember when it comes to motivation. I stress this in all of my coaching and leadership presentations. As managers, we would all agree that work would be so much easier if our employees did what we expected them to do because we asked them to do it. It would be easy to coach and motivate employees if they thought the same way we did, and valued the same things we do. Unfortunately, it just isn't that easy. Steven Reiss found 16 motivational factors, and your top five may not be in line with your employees' top five. That's OK. The problem doesn't occur when they don't match, the problem occurs when you assume they will. In his book, Steven Reiss coined the term "self-hugging," which is the idea that what is potentially best for you is what is potentially best for everyone else. It is the practice of "self-hugging" that gets managers in trouble because they assume if it's important to them, it will be important to their staff. This can create a frustrating experience for the manager.

In all honestly, dogs are much easier to motivate than employees. Dogs tend to be motivated by either food or affection. A dog offers unconditional love.

Feed him and treat him well and he will be by your side following your commands. We have a fence surrounding our back yard with a gate. Even if I kept the gate open, the dogs would stay out back. Where else would they want to go? We feed them and treat them too well for them to want to go anywhere else.

Your employees will require you to dig deeper to recognize their motivational factors. Look at the following employee scenario to put Professor Reiss' motivational list to the test:

Brad is a 21-year-old employee who excels in sales. He displays all of the tendencies of a Type "B" personality: outgoing, energetic and fast-paced, who likes to be around people and craves recognition. Since Brad enjoys "winning" and public recognition, it is a safe assumption he will excel at contests and challenges. While getting to know Brad you discover he is saving money to move into an apartment with his girlfriend. Extra money is now a motivator too. If you look again at Steven Reiss's list, Brad's top motivating desires would be status, acceptance, saving, and social contact. Whenever sales are lagging, Brad's manager has a couple of new tools to use to motivate him to increase his sales.

Satisfied needs don't motivate

Changing your motivational methods is helpful for getting the most out of your employees. If you provide the same thing all the time, be it money, recognition, or free food, then employees may grow to expect it and it will stop being a motivator. Many professionals have read the bestselling book *Who Moved*

My Cheese?[†] as a message about change. The book is also an analogy about satisfied needs. In the beginning of the story, the two mice and two Littlepeople got up early each morning, dressed quickly, and ran through the maze to get their cheese. New cheese was a motivator for them. After a while, the Littlepeople got up later, dressed more slowly, and took their time strolling to the maze for the cheese. After all, it was always there and they were sure it was always going to be there in the future. Their needs were satisfied, so the cheese was no longer a motivator to get up early.

When we took Baleigh to training, many other dog owners used food and treats to motivate their dogs to perform the various commands. Some of the dogs complied, while others didn't. One couple, Frank and Sue, were having trouble with their eight-month-old Golden Retriever, Katie. They were bringing a bag of Katie's dry dog food with them for motivation. Katie loved the food at home, and ate well, so they were surprised when Katie wouldn't sit and stay at training. Katie knew she was getting the food when she went home, so she wasn't too motivated to perform tricks outside of the house for the same reward she would get later for doing nothing. The trainer, Deb, suggested bringing a more desirable treat next time, something Katie wouldn't get at home. The following week Frank and Sue grilled a couple of hot dogs, cut them up into small pieces, and brought them to training. I can honestly say that that was the

---

† Johnson, Spencer; *Who Moved My Cheese?* (G.P. Putnam's Sons, 1999)

most obedient I ever saw Katie. She sat, stayed, rolled over, and would have probably stood on her head if given the command. She was provided a new motivator, and boy did it motivate!

Take a look at the following scenario about satisfied needs.

Fred worked on the sales floor of an electronics store. He was responsible for assisting customers with their questions and determining which products were best for them. Looking to boost sales, the store instituted a "Bonus Bucks" program to incent employees to sell additional products and services such as video cables and extended warranties. Fred was saving to buy a car, so he was eager to earn some extra money. He started talking to customers; developing a well-crafted pitch about how the best television cables will provide a better picture, and explaining the benefits of an extended warranty on a digital camera. He did pretty well, and was earning an extra $300-$400 a month in incentives. After about six months, Fred came to expect the extra money in his paychecks. The money was no longer a bonus; it had become part of his expected salary.

Feeling confident in the extra income, Fred went out and purchased a new car. After months of incentive money, Fred's need to earn extra cash to buy a car had been satisfied. Fred started taking the extra $300-$400 a month for granted, and it no longer motivated him to go out of his way to sell additional products. He was content to provide his customers with only what they asked for, and gradually retired his sales pitch. Come the end of the month, Fred didn't meet his goals for the first time in almost a year. His next paycheck contained $350 less than the month before. Fred was stunned. He didn't relate the decrease in pay to his decrease in sales. In his eyes, his bosses took from him something he was counting on, and felt entitled to receive. The sales program had now created a demotivating environment for Fred and his coworkers. By changing what you use for motivation, your employees won't get used to the same reward and the reward won't become an expectation.

Employees are not motivated by someone else's award

When we go to the pet store and buy a toy, we have to buy two. If we only bring one home, the dogs will fight over it until one of them eventually wins and hides it behind the couch. The purpose of bringing a new toy into the house was to keep both the dogs engaged. Instead, I created conflict between them.

Managers may inadvertently cause conflict in their own departments by creating contests which only one person can win, or which pits one group of employees against another. The thought behind implementing these contests is that the competition will bring out the best in everyone and raise each person's performance to a higher level. It can work for certain businesses and for certain people. For others, it can be a recipe for disaster. Managers need to keep a finger on the pulse of the department to ensure that the competition creates the desired effect. If the same person wins all the time, maybe another will be motivated to be better next time. Maybe other employees give up, knowing they are not going to win. Sometimes contests only motivate the employees who normally win contests. The contest you create to enhance performance can actually have the opposite effect.

Sometimes life imitates art. Maybe you've seen the movie *Glengarry Glen Ross*‡. If your job involves sales, I'm pretty sure you have. If not, it is a really good film with a great supporting cast. In the movie, Alec Baldwin plays Blake, a hotshot sales guru who was brought into the Mitch & Murray real estate office to motivate their four salesmen to increase revenue. In a dramatic scene, Blake gives the salesmen a speech which is part motivating, part intimidating, and part emasculating. Blake tells them of a new contest where first place is a new car, second place is a set of steak knives, and third place is...you're fired! This created an environment of nervousness, despair, and recklessness. There is infighting, back-stabbing, theft, and bribery. All four salesmen knew Ricky Roma (in an Academy-Award nominated performance by Al Pacino) was going to get the most sales anyway, and he didn't even need the contest to be motivated. The others broke every rule they could think of just to save their jobs.

Remember, it's a long season

Baleigh graduated puppy school as one of the best students in her class. You could refer to her as the top dog! We wanted to continue, so Ann and I en-

---

‡ *http://www.imdb.com/title/tt0104348/*

rolled her in advanced training. The first three weeks of the class she did tremendously. The trainer even pointed Baleigh out as an example for others in the class. We couldn't have been prouder puppy parents. Then came week four—Baleigh did not want to cooperate at all. She would get up and walk away when we wanted her to stay, and check out other dogs when we wanted her to heel. It was frustrating and embarrassing. We were dumbfounded; suddenly Baleigh forgot everything she was taught and no amount of treats could motivate her to perform. The trainer told us there was no cause for alarm. Dogs can get tired and bored too, and sometimes they need a break.

It's tough to constantly stay motivated to perform your job at the highest levels. Individuals have off days and lulls in productivity. Think of a baseball season that lasts six months and 162 games. The best hitters go into slumps, and the best teams go on losing streaks. There is an old saying that every team is going to win 54 games and every team is going to lose 54. What you do with the last 54 is the difference between first and last place. If your company is constantly running promotions, then everything is a promotion. I worked for an organization that ran a two-week promotion every month. Employees met their numbers for the two weeks the promotion was running, and didn't for the other two weeks. Some of it was due to the fact that employees coasted during the off-contest times. Sometimes employees had leads but delayed booking the sale until the promotion started. The problem with all of this was that since employees achieved their numbers during the promotion, the manager concluded it must be working. Unfortunately, this led to more promotions which made the situation even worse.

Look at the entire picture. If you work in a demanding environment with lofty goals, know when to lift your foot off the accelerator. Recognize when things that you used as motivating tools no longer motivate, or worse, demotivate. If you have already created a stressful environment, you might want to skip ahead to the chapter entitled "Don't Forget to Let Them Out to Play."

Kimba's Chapter Recap

1. There is a reason PETCO has different types of treats.

2. Employees are motivated by their reasons, not by yours.

3. Satisfied needs don't motivate.

4. Employees are not motivated by someone else's reward.

5. Remember, it's a long season.

"Money can buy you a nice dog, but only love can make him wag his tail."

—*Kinky Friedman*

7
Respect the Old Dogs

One day an old German Shepherd was out in the woods chasing rabbits. Running deeper in the woods he winds up lost. Wandering about trying to find his way home, he notices a panther heading rapidly in his direction with the intention of having lunch. The old German Shepherd recognizes he is in trouble and thinks quickly. Looking around he notices some bones laying on the ground close by and immediately drops to the ground and starts chewing them. As the panther gets within striking distance, the old dog loudly exclaims, "Boy, that was one delicious panther! I wonder if there are any more around here?"

Hearing this, the young panther stops dead in his tracks. A look of terror comes over him and he slinks away into the trees.

"Whew!" says the panther, "That was close! That old German Shepherd nearly had me!"

Meanwhile, a squirrel had been watching the whole scene from a nearby tree. Figuring he can trade his newfound knowledge for protection from the panther, he follows the cat. When the squirrel catches up with the panther he tells him what he knows and strikes a deal for himself with the panther. The young panther is furious at being made a fool. He orders the squirrel to hop on his back as he sets off to seek revenge.

Now, the old German Shepherd sees the panther returning with the squirrel on his back and starts to think about what is he going to do. Instead of running, the dog sits down with his back to his attackers, pretending he hasn't seen them yet. Just as they get close enough to hear, the dog says out loud

"Where's that squirrel? I sent him off an hour ago to bring me another panther!"

The moral of this story: *Don't mess with the old dogs. Brilliance comes with age and experience.*

I found this fable online.* Somebody e-mailed me a link, probably because I own a German Shepherd, or because I like analogies. It could also be because the person is insinuating I am old. It doesn't matter why; all three are accurate. I started using this story in coaching workshops and presentations to illustrate the value that seasoned employees bring to their organization. I also use it when I talk with younger employees who expect to be promoted through the ranks quickly just because they have a college degree or think they are the 'next big thing' to come to work at the company. A college education provides individuals with knowledge, but experience tells them when and how to apply that knowledge. Individuals gain experience by investing their time and honing

---

* "The Old German Shepherd" is a fable of undetermined origin.

their skills in their field of work. Experience can also be gained through the experience of others, the 'old dogs' in the organization.

Respect the old dogs. Their years of experience and knowledge are valuable to other employees in your organization. Your seasoned veterans know the tricks of the trade, they have "been there, done that" and have usually been successful along the way. They can be vital to mentoring younger employees by providing their perspective and wisdom to help others navigate through office politics and the corporate way of life. Valuing veteran employees and using them as resources can even rejuvenate the career of someone stuck in a rut. It will also create a sense of usefulness for an older employee who is concerned about youth taking control of the organization.

According to the U.S. Bureau of Labor Statistics (March 2011), there are 29.5 million workers aged 55 and over.[†] That's a lot of collective experience in the workplace upon which managers can rely. There are also 46.5 million workers aged 18-34. These are your future leaders; individuals who could benefit from the wisdom and advice of the more seasoned employees. Take advantage of the experience, knowledge, and expertise of your "old dogs" to create a mentoring program.

Employees don't take the time to mentor because they either don't think they have anything special to offer other employees or they feel they are too busy to take the time to be a mentor. The fact is, seasoned

---

† *http://www.bls.gov/data/*

employees do have something to offer. Many mentors don't realize the importance of what they know because they already know it. They have developed years of experience in their profession or organization, and over that time have found:

- what works in certain situations and what doesn't.
- what to say in certain situations, how to say it, whom to say it to, and when to shut up!
- who the go-to person is for each situation.
- when the good and the bad times are to approach the boss.
- how to position yourself for advancement.

Being a mentor really doesn't take a lot of time out of an individual's schedule. How long does it take to answer a question or reply to an email? Sometimes, an employee can accomplish a lot as a mentor for less than an hour a week.

The great thing about getting a second dog is that the first will oftentime serve as a mentor. It's easier to housebreak a dog when you already have one who is housebroken. The second dog will follow the lead of the first. If you ever watch Cesar Millan's *The Dog Whisperer*, you will see him bringing a new dog in to interact with his pack. The pack becomes mentors for the new dog, and that dog quickly learns acceptable behavior. I'll discuss more in the next chapter.

In addition to serving as a mentor, seasoned employees can be called upon to serve as SMEs (subject matter experts) to assist with training and development programs. SMEs are often used in training classes to talk with employees about specific areas. The benefit of this is enormous. The class participants are able to get greater detail and hear "war stories" from the people who perform and know the job best. They can get any and all questions answered right on the spot. The SME benefits from a sense of value and usefulness. It also helps break up their day and allows them to get to know and interact with employees they otherwise wouldn't. As a trainer, I benefit because I don't need to research an area with which I'm unfamiliar, or have to follow up to answer questions I couldn't answer in the class. SMEs know their stuff, and sometimes they like to talk and go over their allotted time, or they may use jargon with which participants are unfamiliar. When using an SME it is important to have a trainer or moderator present to keep them on track.

If serving as a mentor or subject matter expert is not for your 'old dogs', you must find other ways to keep them engaged. Talk with them to find out what their career goals are. Older employees' goals tend to vary quite a bit between professional and personal interests. Some of your seasoned employees might still have an eye on promotions, while others may have an eye towards retirement. Don't assume an employee who is no longer interested in being promoted is not interested in thought-provoking and challenging work. I worked with an employee, Ray, who came to the credit union after retiring from a local school district with over 30 years' experience. Ray was new to banking. He wasn't looking for a second career, but did want interesting work and an opportunity to make a difference. He was a hard worker, learned everything he could about the banking industry, and was well-liked by his colleagues and our members. With his work ethic and high level of professionalism, Ray served as a role model for younger, more ambitious employees.

"My age and experience allowed me the leeway of confidence that matched the skill achievement at the branch level" Ray recently told me. "I knew how to find out what I needed to know—using my people skills and basic courtesy to move along in advancement."

As a proud "old dog" in his own right, Ray agrees he is motivated by being appreciated, productive, and stimulated by the work he does. "A successful employee is never too young or too old to exhibit qualities of accomplishment. Usually people will rise to the occasion and demonstrate their value, especially those employees who feel they have something to prove to their superiors and to themselves."

Remember to respect the old dogs. Who better to help show all the tricks to the new puppies? Plus, you never know when you will need their astute wisdom to help outwit a slick panther!

Kimba's Chapter Recap

1. Don't mess with the Shepherd!

2. Develop a mentoring program.

3. Utilize your subject-matter experts.

8
Pavlov's Dog Talks to the Other Dogs

Ivan Petrovich Pavlov was a Russian psychologist during the turn of the 20th Century. In his most famous experiment, Dr. Pavlov studied the correlation between eating and salivating within dogs. During the study, he preceded a meal of meat with various sounds and signals. Pavlov discovered that, after a few sessions, the sounds and signals alone would induce the dogs to salivate. This discovery is known as behavioral conditioning. It states that for every stimulus there is a response.

Our dogs know their food is kept in a closet in the kitchen. Every time we open that door, our dogs run into the kitchen expecting to be fed. They have been conditioned to think that when the door opens, food will come out of it and into their bowls. After they eat, our dogs go to the back door to be let outside. Baleigh learned this routine over time, through repetition. When we got Kimba, he didn't know the routine. He didn't know where the food was kept and what the significance of opening the closet door in the kitchen meant. After only a day at home, he ended up running alongside Baleigh when he heard the door open. Was he smarter than our other dog? A quicker learner? No, he learned his behavioral conditioning from his "colleague." It seems dogs do talk to other dogs.

Pavlov's discovery dictates that for every stimulus there is a response. This concept is also true for employees. Take a moment to look at the following three examples of workplace stimulus and write the first response which comes to mind.

- You ask Fred, an employee with a history of disciplinary issues, to come into your office and to shut the door behind him. What is Fred thinking? What are your other employees thinking?
- You notice Sherry has begun making and/or receiving a number of secretive personal phone calls. What are you thinking?
- You schedule a mandatory staff meeting to discuss the department's new sales goals for the upcoming quarter. What is your staff thinking?

How did you respond to the previous scenarios? Let's look at each one separately.

In the first scenario, Fred has a history of disciplinary issues, so he will probably attribute a closed-door meeting with the boss to being in trouble once again. In this case, his response might be nervousness, fear, or gloom. Maybe Fred will come in defensive and confrontational, knowing he did nothing wrong. Your other employees are probably assuming the "problem child" is getting in trouble once again. You probably answered the second scenario one of two ways. If you have received a few resignation letters in your management career, you were likely thinking Sherry is applying for a new job. If not, then you were thinking she may be having personal problems she needs to deal with privately.

Your answer to the third scenario depends on how goals are set, communicated, and obtained in your organization. If this is a regular occurrence, your employees probably won't think much about it. If you only have "special sales meetings" when goals are drastically increased then your employees might be anxious, in a good or a bad way, about the meeting. If your department has not been meeting its sales goals recently, then your employees may come into the meeting discouraged or resentful.

How you responded to the scenarios above may or may not be the same way your colleagues would have responded. When faced with different situations, our initial responses are derived from lifelong work experiences. Your employees' responses are the same. As the manager, you need to keep your hand on the pulse of the office to determine what your employees are talking and thinking about at all times. Employees react not only to what is happening around them, but also to what they anticipate is going to happen. Perception is reality, and in the workplace it's not only perception but also anticipation that is a reality to employees.

Effective communication in the workplace is vital

to ensure employees are getting the same message, and that the message is accurate. The old adage of "no news is good news" doesn't work in today's environment where rumors and assumptions can go viral in no time. The office grapevine can spread rumors and half-truths, cause panic, and kill employee morale. Employees who do not receive clear news and information from an authorized source are sometimes left to make it up themselves.

We usually bathe the dogs ourselves at home. In the beginning, they weren't too fond of baths; especially Kimba, who has a lot of fur and takes a long time to dry off. Ann would take Kimba into our shower and bathe him first, while Baleigh sprawled on the floor outside in our bedroom. When Kimba was done with his bath and we let him out, he would run around and bark at Baleigh. Soon Baleigh would run away and hide in another room. Obviously, Kimba told Baleigh about the traumatic experience of getting a bath and scared her off. When we would finally corral Baleigh and bathe her, she liked it. She didn't find it nearly as bad as she feared it to be based on her colleague's comments.

Some organizations have a situation where employees interpret the same policy in different ways. Sometimes, like Baleigh and her bath, they are the victims of misinformation from the office grapevine. Managers may feel as though they are one of the guys on the TV show *Mythbusters*, trying to prove or disprove urban-legend procedures. Maybe something similar goes on in your organization. It's like a bad game of "whisper down the lane." One employee says or does something, then another interprets it his or her own way and says or does it a little differently. Before you know it, employees' actions don't resemble the actual procedures in the least bit. This happens even when an organization has a formalized training program, so you can imagine how much worse it could be without one. It's as if employees obtain their training from the University of MSU—Make Stuff Up.

The issue isn't a lack of organized or written procedures; employees could have current procedure manuals right in front of them. It's just that employees sometimes gravitate to doing things others are doing, even if there is no rhyme or reason for doing so. There is a story I heard and that I often tell about how policies and procedures are created. Maybe you can relate to the message in the story, and maybe it happens in your workplace, too.

Scientists placed six monkeys in a room. In the middle of the room was a ladder. Directly over the ladder was a bunch of bananas, hanging from the ceiling. Monkeys like bananas, so before long one of them started to climb the ladder. As soon as the monkey started to climb, ice-cold water sprayed from the ceiling, drenching the other monkeys. This repeated until the monkeys realized that any time one of them climbed the ladder, the others got soaked with ice cold water. Because of this, the monkeys made a pact not to climb the ladder. After a week, one of the monkeys was removed and replaced by a brand new monkey, Bruce. He saw the bananas and was surprised none of his roommates took the initiative to climb to get them, so he started to climb himself. Not wanting to get drenched, the other monkeys ran over and started beating Bruce up as soon as he started his climb. A couple days went by and another of the original monkeys was replaced by a new one, Sam. Again, this new monkey saw the bananas, saw the ladder, and started to climb. Just as before, all of the other monkeys, including Bruce, started to beat him up. Bruce wasn't sure why he was beating Sam up, or why no one was allowed to climb and get the bananas, but everyone else was doing it so he joined in.

Eventually, all of the original monkeys were replaced one by one. None of the monkeys in the room were ever sprayed by the water, yet they all knew if a new one tried to climb up the ladder to grab a banana it was their responsibility to beat him up. It didn't make sense, but that's how things were done around there.

Think about how some of your employees follow the lead of their colleagues, good or bad. A new employee, Nick, was hired right out of school for an entry-level position. Everyone else in the department was a seasoned employee. The only negative thing about the employees was their tendency to arrive at work after the 8:00 starting time. The manager overlooked this, because when they arrived at work each and every employee got down to business, performed at a high level, produced results, and was willing to stay late if needed. After a couple of weeks on the job, Nick began to arrive after 8:00 as well. This didn't sit well with the manager. He wanted to hold Nick to the standard of being on time, even though nobody else was held to the same standard. Nick's attendance now became a coaching issue. The problem was that Nick learned this behavior from the rest of his team. His behavioral conditioning told him it was acceptable to arrive to work late. By not addressing the rest of the employees, the leaders of the pack, the manager created the coaching issue himself.

Kimba's Chapter Recap

1. Your pack talks when you're not around.

2. Employees react to what they anticipate will happen.

3. Honest, timely communication can squash the rumor mill.

Prepare for the Occasional Accident

Anyone who has ever housebroken a dog knows that just when you think you have accomplished the goal, the dog has an accident. Maybe you weren't paying attention when he had to go out, or maybe you left him home alone too long. It's not that the dog has regressed or suddenly forgotten the training. It was an accident which you need to correct. You, in turn, learned to be more observant and prepared the next time.

Hopefully, managers are just as understanding when an employee makes the occasional mistake. Sometimes we put too much responsibility on an employee too soon, or we assign new projects without providing the proper tools and guidance. Occasional mistakes are not necessarily a bad thing; they can provide a learning experience for you and for your employee. Affording an environment where the employee can make the occasional mistake will allow him or her to gain valuable experience and grow and develop internally as an employee.

Understand that all accidents are not created equally. Accidents result in increasing levels of severity. If the dog pees on the tile floor it's an easy mess to clean up. If he does it on the carpet it takes more effort to clean to avoid a lingering issue. If he chews up your leather reclining sofa (as ours did), you have no place to sit.

Employee accidents can lead to various degrees of loss as well. Mistakes which are easily corrected and cause no monetary loss, negative customer experience, or lasting customer ill will are on the low end of the spectrum. With that in mind, constant minor mistakes made by the same employee can create a cumulative issue. If a cashier forgets to give the customer the correct change, correcting the mistake and offering an apology may solve the problem. If the cashier does it again, the customer may doubt the employee's capabilities, or even worse, honesty. This may cause the customer to avoid shopping at the store in the future.

Some employee accidents require short coaching or training sessions with the employee. In recurring or more severe instances, accidents should result in disciplinary actions. The disciplinary action process does not need to be a negative interaction with your employee. If done correctly, a disciplinary action is a necessary part of the coaching and learning process. When our dogs are disobedient, we reprimand them. It's not severe, and later we show them how much we love and appreciate them. It's the same concept with your employee. When conducting a disciplinary action you are communicating that the action needs to stop, and improvements must be made. You are censuring the action, not the employee.

Disciplinary actions fall into three categories: *attendance*, *performance*, and *conduct*. As a manager, it is important to understand the different categories so you can document the issue, know how the disciplinary process should proceed, and determine the level of training, coaching, and mentoring required.

Attendance

When an employee fails to meet the expectation of being at work every day at the expected time, including returning from breaks and lunches. If your company interacts directly with customers and is open more than 40 hours, your employees may have a flexible schedule. If so, their hours may change from day to day or week to week. Regardless of the type of schedule, employees should be expected to work their schedule unless prior arrangements have been made with their supervisor.

In many companies, attendance issues are the number one cause for termination. Each manager has a different standard of what is considered late. Maybe you provide your employees with a five-minute grace period, maybe it's ten. Whatever time you consider is late, please keep it consistent. If you are OK when employees arrive ten minutes late, 8:10 is the new start time. Don't get upset when nobody is in the office at 8:00. Remember the chapter about setting boundaries, because you are now resetting the boundary for attendance.

Performance

When an employee's work performance does not

meet your company's expectations, the performance level of comparable colleagues, or causes a direct negative impact. Performance can be directly measured four ways:

- Quality
- Quantity
- Cost
- Time

A performance issue may be measured by any and all of the above. If an employee submits a report which is poorly written and includes inaccuracies, quality is definitely the first issue. Now that report must be rewritten, and more time is lost. If there is a delay there may be a cost factor as well.

Conduct

When an employee's actions violate the company's policies, standards, or values. Inappropriate conduct may be a one-time occurrence or there may be a pattern of misconduct developing over a period of time. When dealing with issues of conduct, remember to focus on the specific employee behaviors which cause the problem. You can't coach an employee for having a bad attitude. You can coach to the specific behaviors which cause the bad attitude, such as not smiling, or being short and abrupt.

Take the time to document issues as they occur. When approaching human resources with an employee issue you will discover that if the issue wasn't documented, it didn't happen. Documentation provides the manager with a record of specific details of the occurrence. Sufficient documentation allows you to properly collect the facts and eliminate the need to reconstruct the exact details at a later date. It will also provide a reasonable justification for your discipline. All instances should be documented, no matter how incidental or miniscule you think they may be at the time. Small occurences may develop into a pattern of behavior which could lead into larger issues down the road.

Be willing to address employees' mistakes. Don't shy away no matter how uncomfortable this may make you feel. Tactfully helping the employee understand what he or she did wrong and how to do better next time will actually show how much you care. Although many supervisors dread the idea of delivering a disciplinary action, allowing the situation to linger without a formal communication with the employee may only lead to more problems.

- The employee must perform under stress, thinking a more severe reprimand is imminent. This may cause additional performance or conduct issues.
- The employee may believe his conduct is acceptable behavior.
- Other employees may question whether discipline is handled fairly and evenly across the department.
- Once the employee finally receives the action, the reason and details have been forgotten.

Discipline must be immediate, regardless of whether you are dealing with employees or dogs. One evening B.C. (Before Crating), I came home from work to discover pillow feathers everywhere. The dogs got bored, and decided to have a fun time ripping apart a throw-pillow from the sofa. It's funny now, looking back at the pictures I took, but it wasn't then. Baleigh and Kimba greeted me when I walked through the door, the same way they'd greeted me every day before. They were oblivious to the mess they made. For all I knew, they could have done it as soon as I left for work. Dogs don't remember things the same way humans do, so they may have even forgotten the tug-of-war they had with the pillow. As upset as I was, disciplining them would only let me blow off steam, and would do nothing to correct their behavior. Since the purpose of discipline is always to correct behavior, the opportunity to discipline was lost. This is why dog trainers say you must catch the dog in the act of being bad. Otherwise he won't know what he is being reprimanded for.

The disciplinary actions should be in writing, with a copy provided to the employee. Most states and organizations require this. The memo should be written so it is clear, concise, and to the point. Anybody who reads it should be able to understand exactly what occurred and what the ramifications were. Your company might have a standard form for disciplinary actions. Verify with your supervisor or your human resources department. If you are responsible for creating a memo on your own, it should contain these four parts:

- Specifics of the occurrence(s). This should be written in the same format as the recording documentation by focusing on behaviors while including the who, what, where, when, why, and how. Use bullet points to break down multiple occurrences or subplots.

- Policy, standard, or expectation violated. If this is a follow-up from a previous disciplinary action, state the date and expectation of that memo as well.
- Negative impact caused to the organization.
- Result and future expectation(s) of disciplinary action. If the result includes a probationary period, detail the timeframe and consequences if improvement is not made.

When meeting with the employee, ask for his or her ideas to correct the situation. In many instances, the employee will either present a plan which is acceptable to you or ideas that match your own. If so, the employee will be more likely to accept your objectives and work to solve the situation. If not, you must offer your own solutions to the problem. Stress to the employee that your ultimate goal is his or her improvement and long-term success within the organization.

Provide the employee with a timeframe for improvement. Explain if he or she does not show improvement, or if any additional transgressions occur, it will result in further disciplinary actions—up to and including termination. Have the employee sign the disciplinary action memo or form and provide a copy. After the meeting, it is important to follow up with the employee during the timeframe discussed. Note how the employee's performance or conduct during this time compares to performance or conduct which caused the disciplinary action. Praise the employee for any and all improvements made. If the employee continues to struggle, make him or her aware of it. Additional disciplinary actions may be appropriate.

Ensure your employees understand the coaching and feedback you provide is designed to help them grow and succeed at work. While it may be tough for employees to hear constructive criticism about their work performance, they will be more willing to accept and follow your advice if they know you have their best interests at heart.

Kimba's Chapter Recap

1. Mistakes create a learning experience for you and your employee.

2. Address mistakes directly and quickly.

3. Document issues as they occur.

4. Coaching and feedback are designed to help employees grow and succeed at work.

5. Baleigh was the one who ate the pillow.

10
Don't Forget to Let Them Out to Play

As I mentioned previously, we crate our dogs during the day while we are at work. I wasn't keen on the idea at first, but our vet and dog trainer both recommended it, as do a lot of people on online dog forums. Now when we get ready to leave, our dogs go to their crates automatically. Kimba likes it there, and often goes in without coaxing for a little rest between play sessions while we're home. The dogs feel comfortable in their crates, and are receptive to spending time in them during the day. When my wife and I come home, they are ready to get out and release some pent-up energy. Just as we know to crate them before we leave, we also know they need time to go out and play.

I always joke that my dogs would never run away from home—they have it too good here to go anywhere else. Outward appreciation of your staff will go a long way towards retaining your employees. Just like retaining your customer base, employees need to know they are receiving something from your organization that they won't get somewhere else.

The company I work for has been recognized as

one of the best places to work in Pennsylvania by the *Central Penn Business Journal.* In addition to our salary and benefits package, we were lauded for other perks we provide for our employees such as free monthly lunches, gala employee appreciation dinners, summer trips to baseball games and amusement parks, and allowing employees to wear Phillies shirts and jerseys on baseball's opening day and during the playoffs. These are some of the ways we allow our employees to go out and play, and it leaves them energized, engaged, and excited to come to work each day.

If your company operates on a normal Monday-to–Friday, 40-hour schedule, your employees will spend more waking hours during the week at work, or commuting to and from work, than they do at home. For employees to spend so much time in one place it needs to be a place where they feel comfortable. Allowing employees to have fun events and mental excursions at work makes it more enjoyable and ultimately more productive. Mental breaks allow employees to recharge their batteries and refocus their efforts on completing important projects.

Hyland Software takes the concept of letting employees out to play to a new level. This 900-employee organization in northern Ohio allows employees to take advantage of an on-site massage therapist, free fitness center, and a "rejuvenation station" equipped with large recliners and soothing sounds of the ocean. In the summer, employees frequently receive emails from CEO A.J. Hyland alerting them that the ice cream truck is in transit for free snacks. This company takes playing seriously; one of their salaried positions is "Minister of Culture," responsible for creating a pleasurable work experience.

At our house, Kimba is his own Minister of Culture. He likes to go outside to play and will often nip at Baleigh's legs to make sure she runs out and joins him. They like to run around and circle our inground pool, so much so there is a dirt track around the first turn! When it rains, they come in muddy and track the mud through the kitchen and living room, so we switched from carpet to wood floors in the living room. We consider switching flooring and dealing with dirt spots outside as minor concessions to keep our dogs engaged and happy.

You can also find ways to make minor concessions in your workplace to make your employees feel appreciated and have fun at work. The following is a list of ways to show your employees that you care, and give them an opportunity to go out and play. Some may involve a change in company policy, and some involve an investment in money or resources. You'll find that your employees are less impressed by the money spent as they are by the effort you make to appreciate the work they do.

Flextime Schedules

Flextime allows employees to strike a work/life balance by restructuring their work hours accordingly. Instead of working a traditional 8:00-5:00 schedule, with an hour for lunch, employees may work 9:00-6:00, 7:00-4:00, or take a shorter lunch to come in later or leave earlier. Employees may also be afforded the opportunity to work four 10-hour days instead.

Telecommuting

This is an arrangement in which employees can work from home or another offsite location, staying connected by telephone and/or computer. Both flex-time and telecommuting can be popular ways for employees to combat rising fuel costs. Telecommuting also allows employees to contribute during snow days when they might otherwise call off.

Dress-down Days

I mentioned earlier that we allow employees to wear the colors of our local professional sports teams during their respective playoffs. We also allow employees to wear jeans every payday in exchange for a $5 donation to a selected charity.

Community Participation

Encourage employees to get involved with their communities. Volunteer events are a great way for employees to bond outside of work. Big Brothers Big Sisters has a school-based program where they partner with local businesses to spend two hours a month in school with a student. It's a great way to give back to the community, and employees will value the time they spend with their new friends.

Free Food

Do you remember the excitement back in first grade when the milk and cookie cart would come around after lunch with free snacks? There is no better way to get to your employees' heart than through their stomachs. Our dogs get rewarded with treats, why don't your employees? You don't have to provide a full meal, just an occasional snack will do the trick. By the way, snacks always taste better when they are served by the boss.

Create an Outside Oasis

Have a place outside where employees can go to take a walk or eat their lunch. This allows them to get away from work while still at work. You can start with a table and a couple of benches. Look for a space outside to turn unused ground into an employee garden. Employees can plant fruits and vegetables, and can culminate with an employee sale.

Remember Their Milestones

Send out cards for employees' birthdays and anniversaries with your organization.

Pass Along Free Perks

Does your company get free tickets to events for the top executives and salespeople? If so, raffle them off to the entire staff instead. Also, many retailers will offer discounts and coupons to local businesses for shopping, entertainment, health club membership, and more. Take advantage and pass these deals along to your employees.

Remember, your employees are the lifeblood of your organization. Obviously, employees are not pets. Managers need to take time to get to know their employees personally; their likes and interests outside of work, their goals and aspirations. This is the key to motivation. By understanding what drives your employees and what is important to them, you can create an engaging and motivating interaction. A highly engaged, dedicated, and respected staff supplied with the knowledge, ability, and motivation to get the job done will succeed. Your staff's success becomes your success.

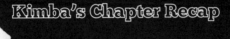

Kimba's Chapter Recap

1. Employees are the life-blood of your organization.

2. Mental breaks allow employees to recharge their batteries and refocus their efforts on completing important projects.

3. Employees will be impressed by the effort you make to appreciate the work they do.

4. Let the dogs out—unleash the hounds!

About the Author

Michael Patterson is a trainer, speaker, and career coach with over twenty years' experience in the banking industry. He has been in the training field for over 11 years, specializing in coaching, leadership, and employee development topics. He is currently responsible for the training and development of a $1.3 billion, 300-employee credit union in southeastern Pennsylvania.

Michael lives in suburban Philadelphia with his wife Ann and their two dogs, Baleigh and Kimba. He is a registered Pennsylvania Interscholastic Athletic Association (PIAA) wrestling referee and former coach.

Michael is an active volunteer with Big Brothers Big Sisters of Bucks County, Pennsylvania. He is an avid sports fan and political junkie.